Application

C000264651

... ...EN SCHOOL FOR GIRLS
Blackfen Road
Sidcup, Kent
DA 15 9NU

BLACKFEN SCHOOL FOR GIRLS
Blackfen Road
Sidcup, Kent
DA15 9NU

Application of Number

Gwyn Davies & Gordon Hicks

Longman

Pearson Education Limited
Edinburgh Gate
Harlow
Essex CM20 2JE, England

and Associated Companies throughout the world

Reprinted 2000

ISBN 0 582 31924 2

British Library Cataloguing-in-Publication Data
A catalogue record for this book is
available from the British Library.

Set by 35 in 10/12 pt Times
Printed in Malaysia, LSP

Contents

Preface

The book has been written to meet the requirements of Key Skills in the Application of Number at levels 2 and 3. The text sets out to explain the arithmetic processes and to prepare students for the external examinations at levels 2 and 3. Accordingly the worked examples and exercises are of a general nature using everyday applications of number rather than relating them to discipline areas. The emphasis throughout is to explain the arithmetic concepts using worked examples and illustrate these with a wide range of diagrams. The exercises have been, in most cases, graded by difficulty.

Except in one or two places the numbers are such that calculations can be worked out without the use of the calculator. Although the value and convenience of a calculator in number work is readily acknowledged, it is considered that using mental and manual arithmetic will lead to a greater understanding of numbers and their application.

Chapters 1 to 9 are based on the level 2 requirements, and chapters 10 to 13 are written for level 3. Answers to exercises are also included at the end of the book.

Our thanks are due, as always, to the staff of Pearson Education, and in particular to Chris Leeding and Rehan Hanif for their support and assistance throughout the preparation of the book.

H.G. Davies
G.A. Hicks
December 1999

1 Introduction to number

1.1 Types of numbers

Arithmetic is a process for handling numbers according to rules of addition, subtraction, multiplication and division. Numbers are used in different ways.

Integers

Integers are whole numbers such as 9, 11, 106 etc. These are numbers used in counting objects, such as the number of matches in a box.

Consider an integer such as

$$4368$$

This number is made up as follows:

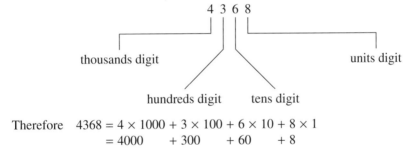

Therefore
$$4368 = 4 \times 1000 + 3 \times 100 + 6 \times 10 + 8 \times 1$$
$$= 4000 \quad + 300 \quad + 60 \quad + 8$$

Proper fractions

Proper fractions are numbers which are less than 1. In Fig. 1.1 the diagram shows a rectangle divided into 8 equal parts.

Fig. 1.1

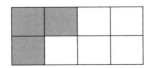

The shaded area is 3 equal parts from the 8 parts, which is written as the proper fraction $\frac{3}{8}$ of the whole rectangle. The top figure 3 is called the *numerator* and the bottom figure 8 the *denominator*.

Decimal fractions

Decimal fractions are numbers less than 1. They are written with a point in front, called the decimal point, such as 0.267. Whereas the digits in whole numbers represent units, tens, hundreds etc., the digits in decimals represent tenths, hundredths, thousandths, etc.

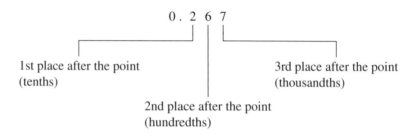

0 . 2 6 7

1st place after the point
(tenths)

2nd place after the point
(hundredths)

3rd place after the point
(thousandths)

Therefore in 0.267

1st place after the point $= \frac{2}{10}$

2nd place after the point $= \frac{6}{100}$

3rd place after the point $= \frac{7}{1000}$

From this definition 0.4 $= \frac{4}{10}$

0.04 $= \frac{4}{100}$ because the 4 is now in the 2nd place.

Square roots and cube roots

Certain numbers can be broken down into a multiplication of two identical integers, such as $4 = 2 \times 2, 9 = 3 \times 3, 16 = 4 \times 4, 25 = 5 \times 5$, etc. Such numbers are called square numbers.

The square root (written as $\sqrt{}$) of a square number will be one of the pair of its identical factors, so that

$$\sqrt{(4)} = 2 \quad \sqrt{(16)} = 4 \quad \sqrt{(100)} = 10$$

Only square numbers have square roots which are integers. The square root of any other number can be obtained by using the $\boxed{\sqrt{}}$ key on an electronic calculator. For example $\sqrt{(42)} = 6.481$ to three places of decimals.

Other numbers can be broken down into a multiplication of three identical integers, such as $8 = 2 \times 2 \times 2, 125 = 5 \times 5 \times 5$, etc.

The cube root (written as $\sqrt[3]{}$) of such a number will be one of the trio of its identical factors, that is $\sqrt[3]{(8)} = 2, \sqrt[3]{(125)} = 5, \sqrt[3]{(1000)} = 10$.

1.2 Prime factors

Certain integers can be broken down into two or more integers multiplied together, such as

$6 = 2 \times 3$

$70 = 2 \times 5 \times 7$

Prime numbers are integers which cannot be written as the multiplication of integers. The following are prime numbers: 2, 3, 5, 7, 11, 13, 17. . . .

When a number is not a prime number it can be broken down into prime numbers, called *prime factors*. Therefore

$4 = 2 \times 2$

The prime factors of 4 are 2 and 2. Similarly

$18 = 2 \times 3 \times 3$

The prime factors of 18 are 2, 3, 3.

For a larger number, such as 60, the prime factors may be obtained by the following rule:

RULE

Divide repeatedly by 2 until it will not divide further then by 3, and so on in turn with 5, 7, 11, 13. . . .

Note: A number is divisible by 2 if it ends in an even number or zero, such as 14, 30.

A number is divisible by 3 if the sum of all its digits is divisible by 3, such as 327.

A number is divisible by 5 if it ends in a 5 or a 0, such as 20, 15.

This method is now used to find the prime factors of 60.

Divide by 2	:	2	60
Divide by 2	:	2	30
Divide by 3	:	3	15
Divide by 5	:	5	5
			1

Therefore $60 = 2 \times 2 \times 3 \times 5$
The prime factors of 60 are 2, 2, 3, 5.

EXAMPLE 1.1

Find the prime factors of 7560.

Solution

Divide by 2	:	2	7560	
Divide by 2	:	2	3780	
Divide by 2	:	2	1890	
Divide by 3	:	3	945	(2 will not divide exactly)
Divide by 3	:	3	315	
Divide by 3	:	3	105	
Divide by 5	:	5	35	(3 will not divide exactly)
Divide by 7	:	7	7	
			1	

Therefore $7560 = 2 \times 2 \times 2 \times 3 \times 3 \times 3 \times 5 \times 7$

1.3 Lowest common multiple (LCM)

The lowest common multiple of two or more numbers is the smallest number into which all of them can divide exactly.

Consider the two numbers 6 and 9. The smallest number into which both these numbers can divide exactly is 18.

Therefore the LCM of 6 and 9 is 18.

The LCM of two or more numbers can be found by first writing them in their prime factors. The LCM is then found from these prime factors. Returning to 6 and 9

$6 = 2 \times 3$

$9 = 3 \times 3$

(i)   Select the highest number of the factor 2 in any of the numbers: 2
(ii) Select the highest number of the factor 3 in any of the numbers: 3×3

Therefore   LCM $= 2 \times 3 \times 3 = 18$.

Example 1.2 shows how this method is used with larger numbers.

EXAMPLE 1.2

Find the LCM of (i) 12, 15, 18   (ii) 32, 48, 72.

Solution

(i) Writing the numbers in prime factors
$$12 = 2 \times 2 \times 3$$
$$15 = 3 \times 5$$
$$18 = 2 \times 3 \times 3$$
The highest number of prime factor 2 is in 12: 2×2
The highest number of prime factor 3 is in 18: 3×3
The highest number of prime factor 5 is in 15: 5

$$\text{LCM} = 2 \times 2 \times 3 \times 3 \times 5 = 180$$

(ii) Writing the numbers in prime factors
$$32 = 2 \times 2 \times 2 \times 2 \times 2$$
$$48 = 2 \times 2 \times 2 \times 2 \times 3$$
$$72 = 2 \times 2 \times 2 \times 3 \times 3$$
The highest number of prime factor 2 is in 32: $2 \times 2 \times 2 \times 2 \times 2$
The highest number of prime factor 3 is in 72: 3×3

$$\text{LCM} = 2 \times 2 \times 2 \times 2 \times 2 \times 3 \times 3 = 288$$

EXERCISE 1.1

1. Write out the following numbers in prime factors:
   12, 32, 30, 72, 96, 124

2. Find the LCM of the following sets of numbers:
   (i) 12, 15 (ii) 15, 25 (iii) 30, 45 (iv) 3, 4, 6
   (v) 12, 15, 18 (vi) 5, 10, 15 (vii) 15, 25, 45 (viii) 27, 54, 81

3. What are the values of:
   $\sqrt{(81)}$, $\sqrt{(64)}$, $\sqrt[3]{(64)}$, $\sqrt[3]{(27)}$

1.4 Negative or directed numbers

Examples of directed numbers

So far in this chapter numbers have been used to denote quantities. By using the + and − signs in front of numbers they can be used to denote opposites or direction.

These numbers are called *directed numbers* and the following are some examples of where they can be used.

(i)   If a person has £20 in a savings account he has +£20; if he is overdrawn in the bank by £50 it is shown as −£50.

(ii) In Fig. 1.2(a) the distance OA measured from left to right is +4 m.
      In Fig. 1.2(b) the distance OB measured from right to left is −5 m.

Fig. 1.2

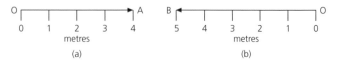

(iii) In the measurement of temperature the freezing point of water is the reference point, which is 0 °C on the Celsius scale. Temperatures above the freezing point will be +°C; temperatures below the freezing point will be −°C.
      In Fig. 1.3(a) the point A indicates a temperature of +22 °C.
      In Fig. 1.3(b) the point B indicates a temperature of −10 °C.

Fig. 1.3

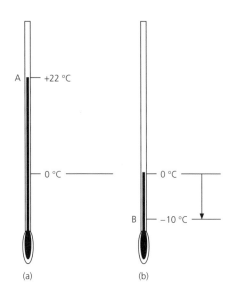

Two ways of using + and − signs

The + and − signs are used with numbers in two ways:

(i)   to denote addition and subtraction of numbers:
      $8 + 4 = 12$
      $9 − 2 = 7$
      $5 − 7 = −2$

(ii) to denote opposites or direction in *directed numbers*:
      +7 or −10

A directed number without a sign is understood to be positive, that is
      $4 = +4$

To distinguish between these two applications it is sometimes useful to place negative numbers in brackets:

(−4), (−9)

Addition and subtraction of negative (−) numbers

Addition

A man has £120 in one bank account but is overdrawn in another account by £80, that is −£80. He therefore has £40 overall.

Total assets = £120 + (−£80) = £40

To get the answer of £40 it is seen that +(−) simplifies to −, that is,

£120 + (−£80) = £120 − £80 = £40

Subtraction

In Fig. 1.4(a) the rise in temperature from A to B is

24 − 10 = 14 °C

that is, the higher temperature minus the lower temperature.

In Fig. 1.4(b) the rise in temperature from A at −18 °C to B at 34 °C is 52 °C:

34 − (−18) = 52 °C

To get the answer of 52 °C it is seen that −(−) simplifies to +, that is,

34 − (−18) = 34 + 18 = 52 °C

Fig. 1.4

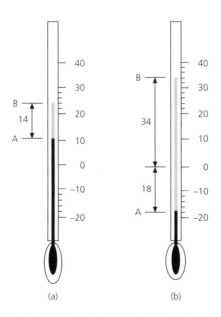

(a)   (b)

The addition and subtraction of negative numbers is carried out according to the following rule:

RULE

Addition of a negative number simplifies to a –, that is +(–) = –
Subtraction of a negative number simplifies to a +, that is –(–) = +

Applying this rule we have

(i) $10 + (-14) = 10 - 14 = -4$
(ii) $8 - (-3)\ =\ 8 + \ 3 = 11$

Further calculations are shown in Examples 1.3 and 1.4.

EXAMPLE 1.3

A thermometer records a temperature rise from -18 °C to -8 °C.
Using the rule for directed numbers determine the temperature rise.

Solution

The temperature rise is

$$-8\ °C - (-18\ °C) = -8 + 18 = +10\ °C$$

This result can be seen in Fig. 1.5 where the rise in temperature is from A to B.

Fig. 1.5

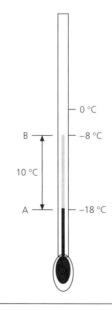

EXAMPLE 1.4

Add and subtract the following directed numbers, using the above rule.

(i) $6 + 7$ (ii) $10 + (-4)$ (iii) $-5 + 3$ (iv) $7 - (-12)$

(v) $-2 + (-4)$ (vi) $-8 - (-3)$ (vii) $8 + (-6)$

Solution

(i) $6 +$ $7 = 13$

(ii) $10 +$ $(-4) = 10 - 4\ =\ 6$

(iii) $-5 +$ $3\ = -2$

(iv) $7 - (-12) =\ 7 + 12 = 19$

(v) $-2 +$ $(-4) = -2 - 4\ = -6$

(vi) $-8 -$ $(-3) = -8 + 3\ = -5$

(vii) $8 +$ $(-6) =\ 8 - 6\ =\ 2$

EXERCISE 1.2

1. Write the following as directed numbers:
    (i) Mr Z owes £10.
    (ii) The wreck was 180 m below sea level.
    (iii) A car travelled 600 yd West to East.
    (iv) The temperature was 50 °C below freezing.

2. Work out the following additions and subtractions:
    (i) $-7 + 8$ (ii) $-4 - 6$ (iii) $9 - 12$ (iv) $-4 + 8$
    (v) $4 - 8$ (vi) $8 - (-7)$ (vii) $-6 - (-4)$ (viii) $11 - (-4)$
    (ix) $-6 + (-8)$

3. (i) The temperature in the UK at noon on a summer's day was 18 °C. At the North
        Pole it was -30 °C. What was the difference between the two temperatures?
    (ii) In mid-winter at midnight the temperature in London was -8 °C and in Edin-
        burgh -15 °C. What was the difference between the two temperatures?

4. On a particular day the midday temperature was 11 °C and at midnight it was 6 °C
    below freezing. What was the change in temperature?

5. A company makes a loss of £40 000 in the first 6 months of a particular year and
    a profit of £30 000 in the second 6 months of the year. Write these as directed
    numbers and calculate the profit or loss over the whole year.

6. Find the difference in the two temperatures shown by each pair of thermometers A
    and B shown in Fig. 1.6.

7. A garage owner has an overdraft at the bank of £12 000. He pays off £2500 of his
    overdraft, but he is also charged £1200 interest by the bank. What is his new
    overdraft? Write these as directed numbers.

Fig. 1.6

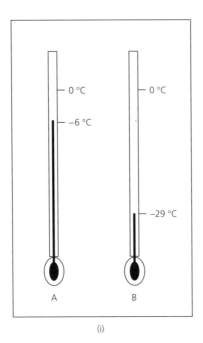

(i)

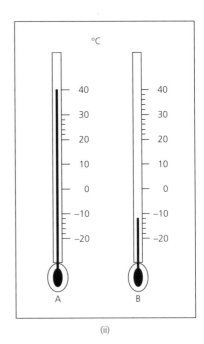

(ii)

8. A student's bank statement was as shown in the table:
Balance at the beginning of the month   −£457.00
Balance at the end of the month   −£537.00
How much had he withdrawn during the month?

9. The highest point of a volcanic island was 459 m above sea level. The top of a submerged mountain close to it was at a depth of −143 m (that is, below sea level). What is the difference in heights between the two peaks?

10. (a) The temperature one winter's evening was −21 °C. It dropped a further 11 °C by midnight. What was the temperature at midnight?
(b) By dawn the temperature was −4 °C, it went up by 12 °C by midday. What was the midday temperature?
(c) What was the temperature difference between midday and midnight?

1.5 Indices

Expressing certain numbers in the form of indices

Indices can be used to write certain numbers in simpler figures. In section 1.3 certain numbers were written in their prime factors. The number 32 in terms of its prime factors is

$$32 = 2 \times 2 \times 2 \times 2 \times 2$$

The number can be written in index form as 2^5 where

  2 is the *base* of the prime factors.
  5 is the *index*, meaning that 2 is multiplied by itself 5 times.

EXAMPLE 1.5

Write the following numbers in index form:
(i) 64   (ii) 81   (iii) 125   (iv) 121

Solution

(i) Writing 64 in prime factors
    $64 = 2 \times 2 \times 2 \times 2 \times 2 \times 2 = 2^6$
(ii) $81 = 3 \times 3 \times 3 \times 3$ $= 3^4$
(iii) $125 = 5 \times 5 \times 5$ $= 5^3$
(iv) $121 = 11 \times 11$ $= 11^2$

Multiplication of numbers in index form

16×8 multiplies out to 128

Written as prime factors this becomes

$$(2 \times 2 \times 2 \times 2) \times (2 \times 2 \times 2) = (2 \times 2 \times 2 \times 2 \times 2 \times 2 \times 2)$$

Rewriting in index form

$$2^4 \times 2^3 = 2^7$$

It can be seen that the multiplication is carried out by adding the two indices, that is,

$$2^4 \times 2^3 = 2^{4+3} = 2^7$$

Note: This can only be done if the two numbers in index form have the same base (in this case both 2).

RULE

Multiplication of numbers in index form on the same base is carried out by adding the indices.

Division of numbers in index form

$729 \div 9$ divides out to 81

Written as prime factors this becomes

$$(3 \times 3 \times 3 \times 3 \times 3 \times 3) \div (3 \times 3) = 3 \times 3 \times 3 \times 3$$

Rewriting in index form

$$3^6 \div 3^2 = 3^4$$

It can be seen that the division is carried out by subtracting the two indices,

that is $3^6 \div 3^2 = 3^{6-2} = 3^4$

Note: This can only be done if the two numbers in index form have the same base (in this case both 3).

RULE

Division of numbers in index form on the same base is carrled out by subtracting the indices.

Note 1:   A number without an index is understood to have an index of 1, that is, $2 = 2^1$

Note 2:   A number with an index 0 is equal to 1, that is, $2^0 = 1$

This can be shown as follows:

$$2^3 \div 2^3 = 2^{3-3} = 2^0$$

But $2^3 \div 2^3 = 1$
Hence $2^0 = 1$

EXAMPLE 1.6

Multiply and divide the following using the rules of indices:
(i) $3^6 \times 3^5$ (ii) $10^2 \times 10^7$ (iii) $8^3 \times 8$ (iv) $4^6 \div 4^2$
(v) $7^8 \div 7$ (vi) $11^4 \div 11^3$ (vii) $9^6 \div 9^6$

Solution

(i) $3^6 \times 3^5 = 3^{6+5}$ $= 3^{11}$
(ii) $10^2 \times 10^7 = 10^{2+7}$ $= 10^9$
(iii) $8^3 \times 8 = 8^3 \times 8^1 =$ 8^4
(iv) $4^6 \div 4^2 = 4^{6-2}$ $= 4^4$
(v) $7^8 \div 7 = 7^8 \div 7^1 =$ 7^7
(vi) $11^4 \div 11^3 = 11^{4-3}$ $= 11^1 = 11$
(vii) $9^6 \div 9^6 = 9^{6-6}$ $= 9^0 =$ 1

---

1. Write the following as prime factors and then in index form.
   (i) 16   (ii) 243   (iii) 625   (iv) 49   (v) 1024

2. Multiply using the rule of indices, leaving the answer in index form.
   (i) $2^6 \times 2^4$ (ii) $10^2 \times 10^4$ (iii) $5^7 \times 5^3$ (iv) $8^6 \times 8$

3. Divide using the rule of indices, leaving the answer in index form.
   (i) $5^7 \div 5^3$ (ii) $6^8 \div 6^5$ (iii) $12^{10} \div 12^9$ (iv) $7^2 \div 7$ (v) $10^4 \div 10^4$

2 Fractions and decimals

2.1 Working with fractions

In Fig. 2.1 the shaded areas are fractions of the whole area.
In (a) the shaded area is 1 part out of 8, that is, $\frac{1}{8}$.
In (b) the shaded area is 3 parts out of 6, that is, $\frac{3}{6}$ which is seen to be $\frac{1}{2}$.
In (c) the shaded area is 8 parts out of 10, that is, $\frac{8}{10}$ which is seen to be $\frac{4}{5}$.
In (d) the shaded area is 6 parts out of 9, that is, $\frac{6}{9}$ which is seen to be $\frac{2}{3}$.

Fig. 2.1

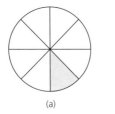 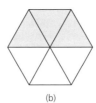  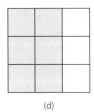

(a)   (b)   (c)   (d)

EXAMPLE 2.1

Show on a shaded diagram each of the following fractions.
(a) $\frac{3}{4}$ (b) $\frac{5}{8}$ (c) $\frac{7}{10}$ (d) $\frac{5}{9}$

Solution

The shaded areas representing these fractions are shown in Fig. 2.2.

Fig. 2.2

  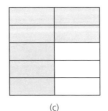 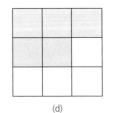

(a)   (b)   (c)   (d)

Simplification of fractions

From Fig. 2.1 it can be seen that fractions can be simplified into smaller numbers. Simplification can be carried out when both numerator and denominator can be divided exactly by the same number.

In the fraction $\frac{3}{6}$ in Fig. 2.1(b), both the 3 and the 6 can be divided by 3,

$$\frac{3}{6} = \frac{1}{2}$$

Similiarly, dividing by 2

$$\frac{8}{10} = \frac{4}{5}$$

EXAMPLE 2.2

Simplify the following fractions.

(i) $\frac{6}{10}$ (ii) $\frac{12}{15}$ (iii) $\frac{10}{15}$

Solution

2 will divide into 6 and 10
$$\frac{6}{10} = \frac{3}{5}$$

3 will divide into 12 and 15
$$\frac{12}{15} = \frac{4}{5}$$

5 will divide into 10 and 15
$$\frac{10}{15} = \frac{2}{3}$$

Addition of fractions

Consider the addition $\frac{1}{2} + \frac{1}{3}$. Both fractions are represented by shaded areas in Fig. 2.3(a). It is impossible to work out what the two shaded areas add up to in order to find the sum of the two fractions.

In Fig. 2.3(b) the square is divided into 6 equal parts, from which it can be seen that the sum of the two shaded areas is $\frac{5}{6}$ of the total area,

Fig. 2.3

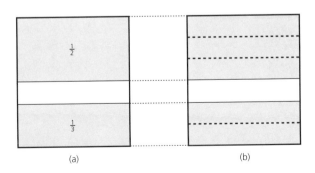

(a)   (b)

---

that is $\quad \frac{1}{2} + \frac{1}{3} = \frac{3}{6} + \frac{2}{6} = \frac{5}{6}$

Now 6 is the LCM of 2 and 3 and this provides a method for adding fractions, which is

(i) Find the LCM of the denominators.
(ii) Change both fractions to have this common denominator.

The method is shown in Example 2.3.

EXAMPLE 2.3

Find the sum of $\frac{3}{4} + \frac{4}{5}$

Solution

LCM = 20
Using the above method $\frac{3}{4} + \frac{4}{5} = \frac{15}{20} + \frac{16}{20} = \frac{31}{20}$
The fraction $\frac{31}{20}$ is now top heavy and is called an *improper fraction*.
This fraction is shown in Fig. 2.4. It is seen to be made up of 1 whole square and
11 parts out of 20 of the other square.

Fig. 2.4

Therefore

$$\frac{31}{20} = 1\frac{11}{20}$$

In this last form it is called a *mixed fraction*.

Addition is now extended to more than two fractions in Examples 2.4 and 2.5.

EXAMPLE 2.4

Find the sum $\frac{2}{3} + \frac{1}{5} + \frac{3}{10}$.

Solution

LCM of 3, 5, 10 $\qquad\qquad = 30$
Make all the denominators $\quad = 30$

$$\frac{2}{3} + \frac{1}{5} + \frac{3}{10} = \frac{20}{30} + \frac{6}{30} + \frac{9}{30} = \frac{35}{30} = 1\frac{5}{30} = 1\frac{1}{6}$$

The addition of mixed fractions is shown in Example 2.5.

EXAMPLE 2.5

Find $2\frac{1}{2} + 1\frac{5}{6} + 3\frac{8}{15}$.

Solution

The whole numbers are added first: $2 + 1 + 3 = 6$

$$2\frac{1}{2} + 1\frac{5}{6} + 3\frac{8}{15} = 6 + \frac{1}{2} + \frac{5}{6} + \frac{8}{15}$$

The fractions are then added as in Example 2.4.
LCM = 30
Make all the denominators = 30.

$$6 + \frac{1}{2} + \frac{5}{6} + \frac{8}{15}$$
$$= 6 + \frac{15}{30} + \frac{25}{30} + \frac{16}{30}$$
$$= 6 + \frac{56}{30}$$
$$= 6 + 1\frac{26}{30}$$
$$= 7\frac{26}{30} = 7\frac{13}{15}$$

Subtraction of fractions

Subtraction of fractions is carried out in the same way as shown in Examples 2.6 and 2.7.

EXAMPLE 2.6

Find the value of $\frac{3}{5} - \frac{1}{4}$.

Solution

LCM of 5 and 4 = 20

$$\frac{3}{5} - \frac{1}{4} = \frac{12}{20} - \frac{5}{20} = \frac{7}{20}$$

EXAMPLE 2.7

Find the value of $5\frac{3}{4} - 1\frac{4}{11}$.

Solution

The first step is to subtract the whole numbers: $5 - 1 = 4$

so that $\qquad 5\frac{3}{4} - 1\frac{4}{11} = 4 + \frac{3}{4} - \frac{4}{11}$

▶

> The LCM of 4 and $11 = 44$
>
> Therefore $4 + \frac{3}{4} - \frac{4}{11} = 4 + \frac{33}{44} - \frac{16}{44}$
> $$= 4 + \frac{17}{44}$$
> $$= 4\frac{17}{44}$$

A sightly more complicated subtraction is shown in Example 2.8.

EXAMPLE 2.8

Find the value of $4\frac{2}{5} - 1\frac{11}{15}$.

Solution

The first step is to subtract the whole numbers: $4 - 1 = 3$
$\text{LCM} = 15$

$$4\frac{2}{5} - 1\frac{11}{15} = 3 + \frac{2}{5} - \frac{11}{15}$$
$$= 3 + \frac{6}{15} - \frac{11}{15}$$
$$= 3 - \frac{5}{15}$$
$$= 2 + 1 - \frac{5}{15}$$
$$= 2 + \frac{15}{15} - \frac{5}{15}$$
$$= 2 + \frac{10}{15}$$
$$= 2\frac{2}{3}$$

EXERCISE 2.1

1. In each of the following fractions state the numerator and denominator in each case.

   (i) $\frac{1}{7}$ (ii) $\frac{3}{4}$ (iii) $\frac{19}{3}$

2. In each of the diagrams in Fig. 2.5, what fraction of the total area has been shaded?

Fig. 2.5

(i)

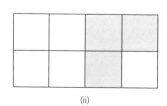

(ii)

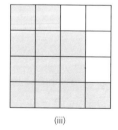

(iii)

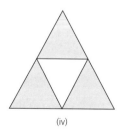

(iv)

3. By simplifying the fractions find the value of x in each case.

   (i) $\frac{4}{12} = \frac{x}{3}$ (ii) $\frac{15}{6} = \frac{x}{2}$ (iii) $\frac{8}{12} = \frac{2}{x}$ (iv) $\frac{14}{49} = \frac{2}{x}$

4. Simplify the following fractions.

   (i) $\frac{9}{12}$ (ii) $\frac{21}{28}$ (iii) $\frac{25}{35}$ (iv) $\frac{36}{45}$ (v) $\frac{42}{54}$

5. Write the following as improper (top heavy) fractions.

   (i) $2\frac{1}{2}$ (ii) $3\frac{3}{4}$ (iii) $5\frac{2}{7}$ (iv) $1\frac{7}{8}$ (v) 8 (vi) 10

6. Write the following as mixed fractions.

   (i) $\frac{14}{9}$ (ii) $\frac{21}{10}$ (iii) $\frac{11}{6}$ (iv) $\frac{100}{9}$ (v) $\frac{19}{13}$ (vi) $\frac{7}{3}$

7. Work out the following additions.

   (i) $\frac{3}{7} + \frac{2}{5}$ (ii) $\frac{3}{4} + \frac{2}{3}$ (iii) $\frac{3}{10} + \frac{4}{5} + \frac{1}{2}$ (iv) $\frac{3}{8} + \frac{5}{6} + \frac{3}{4}$

   (v) $\frac{5}{7} + \frac{2}{14} + \frac{11}{21}$ (vi) $4\frac{1}{9} + 2\frac{1}{3} + 1\frac{7}{12}$ (vii) $2\frac{1}{4} + 3\frac{1}{5} + 4\frac{1}{10}$

8. Carry out the following subtractions.

   (i) $\frac{5}{7} - \frac{2}{5}$ (ii) $\frac{7}{16} - \frac{3}{8}$ (iii) $\frac{4}{5} - \frac{2}{25}$ (iv) $\frac{5}{6} - \frac{7}{9}$ (v) $2\frac{2}{3} - 1\frac{1}{4}$

   (vi) $4\frac{7}{15} - 1\frac{3}{20}$ (vii) $2\frac{2}{3} - 1\frac{1}{5}$ (viii) $2\frac{1}{11} - 1\frac{2}{33}$ (ix) $3\frac{1}{4} - 1\frac{4}{5}$ (x) $2\frac{2}{3} - 1\frac{7}{9}$

9. Evaluate the following.

   (i) $2\frac{3}{4} - 1\frac{7}{16} + 2\frac{1}{8}$ (ii) $2\frac{3}{5} + 1\frac{4}{15} - 3\frac{3}{20}$ (iii) $1\frac{1}{3} + 4\frac{7}{12} - 2\frac{5}{6}$

   (iv) $3\frac{1}{4} - 2\frac{2}{3} + 1\frac{7}{12}$ (v) $6\frac{3}{10} - 2\frac{4}{25} - 1\frac{2}{5}$

10. Four students share a flat. They pay rent according to the size of their bedrooms. The fractions of the rent paid by three students are $\frac{5}{14}$, $\frac{2}{7}$, $\frac{4}{21}$. What fraction does the fourth student pay?

11. Three rooms in a hotel are to be carpeted. The areas of the three rooms are $24\frac{1}{5}$ m², $18\frac{3}{4}$ m², $19\frac{7}{10}$ m². Find the total area of the three rooms.

12. A wholesaler bought $3\frac{1}{2}$ tonne of potatoes and a further $2\frac{1}{4}$ tonne, but later returned $1\frac{1}{3}$ tonne as below standard. What weight did he actually keep?

13. At a craft fair three stalls used $7\frac{1}{4}$ units, $8\frac{1}{10}$ units and $3\frac{1}{5}$ units of electricity on a certain day. What were the total units of electricity used?

    The following day the units used were $6\frac{1}{3}$, $4\frac{1}{4}$, $4\frac{5}{6}$. What was the difference in the electricity used in the two afternoons?

Multiplication of fractions

Consider the multiplication $\frac{1}{2} \times \frac{1}{3}$

In Fig. 2.6 let AB be $\frac{1}{2}$ the horizontal side of a square and AC be $\frac{1}{3}$ of the vertical side. Therefore

$$\tfrac{1}{2} \times \tfrac{1}{3} = AB \times AC$$

This multiplication produces the small shaded area, which is seen to be 1 part out of 6, that is $\frac{1}{6}$ of the whole square.

Therefore $\frac{1}{2} \times \frac{1}{3} = \frac{1}{6}$

Fig. 2.6

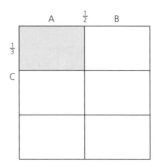

From this result it is seen that the multiplication of fractions is carried out by multiplying the two numerators together and the two denominators together, that is

$$\tfrac{1}{2} \times \tfrac{1}{3} = \tfrac{1 \times 1}{2 \times 3} = \tfrac{1}{6}$$

EXAMPLE 2.9

Find the value of $\tfrac{7}{12} \times \tfrac{3}{14}$.

Solution

The fractions are first simplified: 7 will divide into 7 and 14; 3 will divide into 3 and 12.

$$\overset{1}{\underset{4}{\cancel{\tfrac{7}{12}}}} \times \overset{1}{\underset{2}{\cancel{\tfrac{3}{14}}}} = \tfrac{1 \times 1}{4 \times 2} = \tfrac{1}{8}$$

When the two fractions to be multiplied are mixed fractions they must first be changed into improper fractions as shown in Example 2.10.

EXAMPLE 2.10

Multiply out $2\tfrac{1}{5} \times 2\tfrac{1}{7}$.

Solution

First, convert the fractions into improper ones and then simplify by dividing top and bottom by 5.

$$2\tfrac{1}{5} \times 2\tfrac{1}{7} = \tfrac{11}{\underset{1}{\cancel{5}}} \times \overset{3}{\cancel{\tfrac{15}{7}}}$$

$$= \tfrac{11 \times 3}{1 \times 7} = \tfrac{33}{7} = 4\tfrac{5}{7}$$

1. $\frac{2}{9} \times \frac{3}{4}$ 2. $\frac{7}{12} \times \frac{3}{14}$ 3. $\frac{9}{10} \times \frac{20}{27}$ 4. $\frac{3}{5} \times \frac{15}{12}$

5. $2\frac{3}{4} \times 1\frac{1}{11}$ 6. $3\frac{1}{8} \times 2\frac{2}{5}$ 7. $4\frac{2}{7} \times 5\frac{5}{6}$ 8. $1\frac{2}{5} \times 1\frac{1}{14}$

9. The corridor in an office measures $3\frac{1}{5}$ m $\times$ $2\frac{1}{2}$ m. The carpet in it measures $2\frac{3}{5}$ m $\times$ $1\frac{2}{3}$ m. What area is not covered by the carpet?

Division of fractions

If we divide 30 by 3 we are finding how many threes there are in 30, which is 10:

$30 \div 3 = 10$

Similarly if we divide 2 by $\frac{1}{4}$ we are finding how many quarters there are in 2, that is

$2 \div \frac{1}{4} = 8$

Two squares are shown in Fig. 2.7, each of which has been divided into quarters, making 8 quarters in total.

Fig. 2.7

From this example it is possible to obtain a method for dividing fractions without drawing diagrams.

The fraction we are dividing by, that is, to the right of the $\div$ sign, is inverted and the division sign changed to a multiplication sign.

Then $2 \div \frac{1}{4}$ becomes $\frac{2}{1} \times \frac{4}{1} = \frac{2 \times 4}{1 \times 1} = 8$

EXAMPLE 2.11

Find the value of $\frac{4}{5} \div \frac{2}{5}$

Solution

Using the above method, and simplifying

$\frac{4}{5} \div \frac{2}{5} = \frac{\overset{2}{\cancel{4}}}{\cancel{5}} \times \frac{\cancel{5}}{\cancel{2}} = \frac{2 \times 1}{1 \times 1} = 2$

When mixed fractions are divided they must first be turned into improper fractions and then the above method used, as shown in Example 2.12.

EXAMPLE 2.12

Divide $3\frac{3}{5}$ by $2\frac{7}{10}$.

Solution

Changing to improper fractions and inverting the fraction on the right gives

$$3\frac{3}{5} \div 2\frac{7}{10} = \frac{18}{5} \div \frac{27}{10}$$

$$= \frac{\overset{2}{\cancel{18}}}{\underset{1}{\cancel{5}}} \times \frac{\overset{2}{\cancel{10}}}{\underset{3}{\cancel{27}}}$$

$$= \frac{2 \times 2}{1 \times 3} = \frac{4}{3} = 1\frac{1}{3}$$

EXERCISE 2.3

1. $\frac{3}{5} \div \frac{7}{10}$ 2. $\frac{2}{3} \div \frac{5}{6}$ 3. $\frac{5}{7} \div \frac{10}{21}$ 4. $5\frac{1}{3} \div 2\frac{2}{9}$

5. $1\frac{2}{3} \div 1\frac{1}{4}$ 6. $4\frac{2}{5} \div 1\frac{1}{10}$ 7. $3\frac{3}{4} \div 2\frac{1}{2}$ 8. $1\frac{5}{6} \div 16\frac{1}{2}$

9. In order to make tablecloths, strips of linen $1\frac{5}{6}$ m wide are required. How many strips can be obtained from a piece of cloth $16\frac{1}{2}$ m wide?

10. The barman in a public house took £$9\frac{7}{10}$ in petty cash to buy serviettes at £$\frac{3}{5}$ per packet. How many packets could he buy?

2.2 Decimal numbers

Addition and subtraction of decimal numbers

Addition and subtraction of decimal numbers can be carried out in the same way as for integers. The important thing to remember is to line up the decimal points as shown in Examples 2.13 and 2.14.

EXAMPLE 2.13

Find the value of $13.57 + 247 + 62.491$.

Solution

The decimal points are lined up, and zeros added after the decimal point to assist with the layout.

```
   13.570
  247.000
   62.491
  323.061
```

EXAMPLE 2.14

Evaluate $472.6 - 45.27$.

Solution

Line up the decimal points and add a 0 to the end of the first number, again to assist with the layout.

```
  472.60
   45.27
  427.33
```

Multiplication of decimal numbers

Multiplication of decimal numbers is carried out in the same way as for whole numbers, by ignoring the decimal point in the first instance and inserting it at the end, as shown in Example 2.15.

EXAMPLE 2.15

Work out 5.32×2.6

Solution

Step 1: Multiply the two numbers, ignoring the decimal points in the first instance.

```
    532
     26
   3192
  10640
  13832
```

Step 2: Count the total number of decimal places in both numbers, which is $2 + 1 = 3$.

Step 3: The answer will then have 3 decimal places, that is,

13.832

Division of decimal numbers

Division of decimal numbers is carried out by first making the dividing number a whole number, by moving the decimal points the same number of places in both numbers, as shown in Example 2.16.

EXAMPLE 2.16

Find $366.24 \div 3.2$

Solution

The dividing number 3.2 is made a whole number by moving the decimal point one place to the right in both numbers.

$$366.24 \div 3.2$$

```
        114.4
32 | 3662.4
     32
     46
     32
     142
     128
      14 4
      12 8
       1 6
```

The division can be carried on to more decimal places by adding 0's such as 3662.400. . . .

Conversion of decimal fractions to proper fractions

To change a decimal fraction to a proper fraction, the denominator will be 10, 100, 1000, etc. as shown in the following examples, where the number of zeros in the denominator is the same as the number of decimal places.

$0.7 \quad = \frac{7}{10} \quad$: 1 decimal place

$0.39 \quad = \frac{39}{100} \quad$: 2 decimal places

$0.231 = \frac{231}{1000} \quad$: 3 decimal places

$0.03 \quad = \frac{3}{100} \quad$: 2 decimal places

Conversion of proper fractions to decimal fractions

A proper fraction can be converted into decimals by dividing the numerator by the denominator as shown with the fraction $\frac{3}{8}$. Add as many zeros after the decimal point in the numerator as the number of places required in the decimal fraction.

$$8 \overline{)\begin{array}{l} 3.000 \\ \hline 0.375 \end{array}}$$

EXAMPLE 2.17

Convert $\frac{11}{15}$ into decimals as far as two decimal places.

Solution

Since the answer is required to 2 places of decimals the division is carried out to 3 places, and then the answer is rounded off as described in the next section. Add three zeros to the numerator.

$$
\begin{array}{r}
0.733 \\
15\overline{)11.000} \\
\underline{10.5} \\
50 \\
\underline{45} \\
50 \\
\underline{45} \\
5
\end{array}
$$

$\frac{11}{15} = 0.73$

EXERCISE 2.4

1. Convert the following to proper fractions and simplify wherever possible.
   (i) 0.4   (ii) 0.75   (iii) 0.36   (iv) 0.525   (v) 0.44   (vi) 3.72

2. Convert the following to decimals as far as 3 places of decimals.
   (i) $\frac{5}{8}$ (ii) $\frac{2}{9}$ (iii) $\frac{7}{8}$ (iv) $\frac{2}{17}$ (v) $1\frac{7}{20}$

2.3 Significant figures and rounding off

The number of significant figures is the number of digits making up the number, but excluding any zeros on the left of that number. However, zeros that come on the right of a number may contribute to the number of significant figures. Zeros in the middle of a number will contribute to the number of significant figures.

For example   34 721   has 5 significant figures
                0.034   has 2 significant figures
                0.2   has 1 significant figure
                0.20   has 2 significant figures
                403   has 3 significant figures.

Rounding off means reducing the number of significant figures. With whole numbers rounding off means working to the nearest 10, 100 or 1000, etc. For example, a car dealer buys a second-hand car with 12 213 miles on the clock.

12 213 is a number with 5 significant figures

He may only be interested in the mileage to the nearest 1000, that is, 12 000, in which case

12 000 has been rounded off to 2 significant figures.

A second car has a mileage of 21 934 on the clock. To the nearest 1000, that is to 2 significant figures, the mileage is nearer to 22 000 than 21 000. This leads to a rule for rounding off.

RULE

(i) If the figure being rounded is 5 or greater the preceding figure is increased by 1.
(ii) If the figure being rounded is less than 5 the preceding figure is unchanged.

The use of this rule is shown in Example 2.18.

EXAMPLE 2.18

Round off the following numbers.

(i) 236 to 2 significant figures
(ii) 5149 to 2 significant figures
(iii) 4.095 to 3 significant figures
(iv) 41 780 to 1 significant figure
(v) 0.00716 to 2 significant figures

Solution

Using the above rule:

(i) To 2 significant figures 6 is being rounded off so 1 is added to the preceding figure 3, that is,
236 is rounded off to 240

(ii) To 2 significant figures the figure 4 is rounded off so the preceding figure is unchanged, that is,
5149 becomes 5100

(iii) To 3 significant figures the figure 5 is rounded off so 1 is added to the preceding figure 9, that is,
4.095 becomes 4.10

(iv) To 1 significant figure the figure 1 is rounded off so that
41 780 becomes 40 000.

(v) To 2 significant figures the figure 6 is rounded off so that 1 is added to the preceding figure 1, that is,
0.00716 becomes 0.0072

EXAMPLE 2.19

The digital counter shown in Fig. 2.8 is the mileage of a car, the last figure being tenths of a mile. Express this mileage (i) to 5 significant figures, (ii) to 3 significant figures, (iii) to the nearest 1000 miles, stating the number of significant figures.

Fig. 2.8

Solution

The mileage has 6 significant figures. The zero is on the left and therefore does not contribute to the number of significant figures.

(i) To 5 significant figures the mileage is 64 278.
(ii) To 3 significant figures the figure 7 is rounded off so that 1 is added to the preceding figure 2, that is, 64 300.
(iii) To the nearest 1000 miles the number is 64 000, that is to 2 significant figures.

EXAMPLE 2.20

The ruler shown in Fig. 2.9 is graduated in centimetres and millimetres. From the diagram find the length of the rod AB and express it to (i) 3 significant figures, (ii) the nearest centimetre.

Fig. 2.9

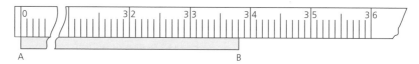

Solution

(i) Length of AB = 33.8 cm to 3 significant figures
(ii) Since the end B is closer to the 34 mark than it is to the 33 mark, length of AB = 34 cm to the nearest centimetre.

EXERCISE 2.5

Round off the following numbers to the number of significant figures stated.

1. 423 to 1 significant figure

2. 628 to 2 significant figures

3. 4735 to 2 significant figures

4. 708 to 2 significant figures

5. 12 459 to 4 significant figures

6. 55 957 to 3 significant figures

7. 43 657 to 3 significant figures

8. 0.00704 to 2 significant figures

9. 18.0581 to 3 significant figures

10. 347.9 to 2 significant figures

11. Find the length of the rod DE in Fig. 2.10 to the nearest centimetre.

Fig. 2.10

12. Fig. 2.11 shows the mileage of a car. Express the number (i) to 5 significant figures, (ii) to 4 significant figures, (iii) to 3 significant figures, (iv) to 2 significant figures, (v) to 1 significant figure.

Fig. 2.11

2.4 Accuracy of a number

If a rod is quoted as 27 cm long it is given to 2 significant figures. However, since any length from 26.5 cm up to 27.5 cm will round off to 27 cm it means that the rod could be any length in this range. Therefore with 2 significant figures the second figure could be in error.

Fig. 2.12 illustrates the point that the end of the rod could be anywhere within the shaded region.

The last significant figure of any number will always have an error range like this. If the length of the rod had been given to 3 significant figures, say 27.3 cm, then by the same conclusion the actual length could be anywhere in the range 27.25 cm up to 27.35 cm, which is more accurate. Therefore the greater the number of significant figures the greater the accuracy.

Fig. 2.12

It is misleading to give a measurement, or an answer to a calculation, to more significant figures than can be justified. In the case of a calculation the answer should not be given to more significant figures than the smallest number of significant figures in the original data.

EXAMPLE 2.21

If the width of a door is expressed as 76 cm, correct to 2 significant figures, what are the smallest and the largest widths the door could be?

Solution

To 2 significant figures the width of 76 cm could apply to any door with a width in the range from 75.5 cm up to 76.5 cm.

The narrowest door could be 75.5 cm
The widest door could be 76.5 cm

2.5 Estimations

In many circumstances it can be useful to estimate the answer to a calculation. This can be done by using approximate values for the numbers. It can be used, for example, to make a quick check if the answer on a calculator is reasonable. The method can also be useful to get a rough estimate of an answer to a calculation. The following are some examples of such estimating:

$948.2 + 17.3$ is approximately $950 + 17 = 967$
9.6×6.13 is approximately $10 \times 6 = 60$
$148.5 \div 1.89$ is approximately $150 \div 2 = 75$
12.46×0.102 is approximately $12 \times 0.1 = 1.2$

EXAMPLE 2.22

The total of the following sums of money

£9.37, £8.45, £3.25, £7.69, £11.36, £12.58

was given as £58.70. Make an approximate calculation to check if the total is likely to be correct.

Solution

The sums of money are approximated to

£9, £9, £3, £8, £11, £13 which added gives £53

▶

There is a large discrepancy between the approximate total and the calculated total, which suggests an error in the calculated total. A recalculation gives a total of

£52.70

EXAMPLE 2.23

The following calculation was made on a calculator:

$$\frac{7.2 \times 9.8}{3.7 \times 2.14}$$

and the answer found to be 0.891. Check the result by doing the calculation with approximate numbers.

Solution

Approximate values are chosen which to the calculation

$$\frac{7 \times 10}{3.5 \times 2} = 2 \times 5 = 10$$

This shows that the answer found using the calculator is wrong and a recheck showed the actual answer to be 8.91.

EXAMPLE 2.24

Estimate the value of

$$\frac{1700 \times 0.0183}{5.2 \times 0.78}$$

and compare the result with the exact calculation using a calculator.

Solution

Approximating the figures to make the calculation easier

$$\frac{1700 \times 0.02}{5 \times 0.8} = \frac{34}{4} = 8.5$$

Using the calculator the result is 7.7 correct to 2 significant figures, showing reasonable agreement.

EXERCISE 2.6

1. Using approximations estimate the value of the following sum. Compare with the exact calculation.

    3.9 + 3.9 + 5.2 + 16.3 + 21.8

2. Estimate the following and compare your estimate with the exact answers.

   (i) $37.1 - 16.2 + 15.67$
   (ii) $48.2 + 16.9 + 18 - 8.45$
   (iii) 30.03×19.7
   (iv) $80.16 \div 4.8$
   (v) £12 995 + £1820
   (vi) 21.4×0.61
   (vii) $1.73 \div 0.95$
   (viii) 6105×10.31

3. Estimate the approximate value of each of the following, and compare your estimates with the exact answers.

   (i) $\dfrac{10.6 \times 19.7}{41.7 \times 2.57}$

   (ii) $\dfrac{11.6 \times 22.4}{5.1 \times 9.2}$

   (iii) $\dfrac{131.6 \times 49.2 \times 16.3}{63.2 \times 38.2}$

   (iv) $\dfrac{723 \times 0.389}{88 \times 1.09}$

   (v) $\dfrac{9180}{29 \times 63}$

   (vi) $\dfrac{359.2 \times 0.22}{11.9 \times 19.13}$

4. Tap washers cost 19p each. I have £6 in my pocket. By making an estimation, check if I have enough money to buy 29 washers.

5. A student earns £16.80 per week in a part-time job. By estimating check to see if he will have enough money after 21 weeks to buy a second-hand car costing £315.

6. Cheese in a supermarket costs £3.27 a kilogram. Work out roughly how much 9.3 kg will cost and check how close your estimate is to the correct cost.

3 Ratio, proportion and percentage

3.1 Ratio

The meaning of ratio can best be explained using mixtures of materials.

Concrete is a mixture of sand, cement and chippings. For consistency and strength the amounts of the various ingredients need to be known.

Consider mixing concrete with 1 bucket of cement, 2 buckets of sand and 3 buckets of chippings. The mixture is 1 part cement, 2 parts sand and 3 parts chippings, that is, in the ratio 1 to 2 to 3, written 1:2:3.

In calculations involving ratios the important step is to find the total number of parts. The total number of parts in the mixture is $1 + 2 + 3 = 6$ as shown in Fig. 3.1.

Fig. 3.1

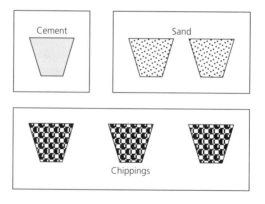

Hence   1 part in 6, that is, $\frac{1}{6}$ of the mixture is cement

2 parts in 6, that is, $\frac{2}{6}$ of the mixture is sand

3 parts in 6, that is, $\frac{3}{6}$ of the mixture is chippings

Therefore in 30 buckets of the mixture there would be

$\frac{1}{6} \times 30 = 5$ buckets of cement

$\frac{2}{6} \times 30 = 10$ buckets of sand

$\frac{3}{6} \times 30 = 15$ buckets of chippings

EXAMPLE 3.1

A length of wooden plank 280 cm long is sawn into 2 pieces in the ratio 3:4. What is the length of each piece?

Fig. 3.2

3 : 4

Solution

First, we find the total number of parts in the ratio.
The ratio 3:4 means 3 parts and 4 parts.
Total number of parts = 3 + 4 = 7
The plank is shown in Fig. 3.2 marked into 7 lengths, so that one of the pieces is 3 lengths and the other is 4 lengths.
Therefore

one piece is $\frac{3}{7}$ of the whole length
the other piece is $\frac{4}{7}$ of the whole length

The lengths of the two pieces are

$\frac{3}{7} \times 280 = 120$ cm

$\frac{4}{7} \times 280 = 160$ cm

EXAMPLE 3.2

A reception drink is made from the following ingredients:

white wine	3 parts
lemonade	5 parts
orange juice	1 part
gin	1 part

To make a bowl of 200 c*l* of this drink, what quantity of each ingredient is required?

Solution

The total number of parts is 3 + 5 + 1 + 1 = 10. Therefore the drink contains

$\frac{3}{10}$ of white wine   = $\frac{3}{10} \times 200$ =   60 c*l*

$\frac{5}{10}$ of lemonade   = $\frac{5}{10} \times 200$ = 100 c*l*

$\frac{1}{10}$ of orange juice = $\frac{1}{10} \times 200$ =   20 c*l*

$\frac{1}{10}$ of gin   = $\frac{1}{10} \times 200$ =   20 c*l*

3.2 Reduction of ratio to simplest form

If the numbers of a ratio can be divided by a common factor it can be converted into a simpler form. For example if a sum of money were to be divided between two people in the ratio 4:6, it is seen that 2 will divide exactly into both numbers. The ratio then simplifies to 2:3.

EXAMPLE 3.3

Simplify the ratios (i) 12:21   (ii) 15:25   (iii) 14:28:35

Solution

(i) 3 will divide into both numbers of the ratio,   12:21   becomes 4:7
(ii) 5 will divide into both numbers of the ratio,   15:25   becomes 3:5
(iii) 7 will divide into the three numbers of the ratio, 14:28:35 becomes 2:4:5

EXAMPLE 3.4

A metal rod 200 cm long is to be cut into 2 pieces in the ratio 4:12. What is the length of each piece?

Solution

Since 4 will divide into both numbers of the ratio, 4:12 simplifies to 1:3.

The total number of parts of the rod is now $1 + 3 = 4$.
The shorter section of the rod is 1 part out of 4 $= \frac{1}{4}$ of 200 = 50 cm.
The longer section of the rod is 3 parts out of 4 $= \frac{3}{4}$ of 200 = 150 cm.

EXERCISE 3.1

1. Simplify the ratios   (i) 15:25   (ii) 21:28   (iii) 15:18:24

2. Simplify the following ratios:
    (i) £4:£10:£12   (ii) $1\frac{1}{2}$:$4\frac{1}{2}$:6
    (iii) £2.50:£5.00:£10   (iv) 6 cm:9 cm:15 cm

3. (i) Divide £4500 in the ratio 4:5.
    (ii) Divide £84 in the ratio 7:3:2.

4. The cost of petrol on a car journey is £96. It is shared by two people in the ratio 5:7. Find how much each of them pays.

5. Three people in a syndicate shared a football pools win of £6000, in the ratio 3:5:7. What sum of money did each person receive?

6. A sack of potatoes weighing 25 kg is divided into two bags in the ratio 2:3. What is the weight of each bag?

7. 5000 bricks are delivered to two neighbours whose requirements are in the ratio 9:16. How many bricks will each neighbour receive?

8. Two boys received pocket money each week from their father, always in the ratio of their ages which were 12 and 10 years. He gave them a total of £11 each week. What did each boy receive weekly?

    Two years later he increased the total each week to £13. What did each boy receive now?

9. 6 waiters and 7 waitresses share the tips received in a restaurant. The total received is £52. How much was distributed to the waiters and waitresses?

10. The garden shown in Fig. 3.3 is divided along its length into lawn and vegetables in the ratio 6:3. Find the length of each part of the garden.

Fig. 3.3

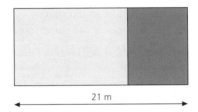

21 m

11. A hot drink was made of 4 parts of whisky and 3 parts of water. In a jug containing 91 *cl* of the drink, how much whisky did it contain?

12. A garage has a franchise for Ford and Nissan cars. It has found that it sells these cars in the ratio 7:3. If in any one month the garage sells 230 cars in total, how many of each car were sold?

13. In an engineering workshop two machines turned out tools in the ratio 10:15. In a particular month 150 tools were produced. How many did each machine turn out?

14. A syndicate of 3 people in the National Lottery had a win of £19 800. The money was shared in the ratio of their payments each week, which were £6, £4, £8. Find (i) the simplest ratio, (ii) how much each person received.

3.3 Direct proportion

If the cost of 3 computers is £1800, the cost of 6 computers will be £3600. As the number of computers is doubled, the cost is doubled. The cost increases in the same ratio as the number of computers increases. The cost and the number of computers are said to be directly proportional to one another.

In general, if the increase in one quantity causes an increase in another quantity in the same ratio, or the decrease in one causes a decrease in the other in the same ratio, the two quantities are in *direct proportion* to one another.

The starting point in such calculations is to write out the two statements, as shown in Examples 3.5 and 3.6.

EXAMPLE 3.5

A college bought 3 computers for £1800. Find the cost of buying 5 computers if the cost per computer is the same.

Solution

Writing out the two statements:

3 computers cost £1800
5 computers cost   ?

The cost is directly proportional to the number of computers purchased.
The number of computers is in the ratio $\frac{5}{3}$.
Therefore the costs are also in the same ratio $\frac{5}{3}$.

Cost of 5 computers $= \frac{5}{3} \times £1800 = £3000$

EXAMPLE 3.6

The ingredients for a meal for 20 people cost £140. What would be the cost of ingredients for the same meal for 15 people?

Solution

The cost of ingredients is directly proportional to the number of people.
Writing out the two statements:

Ingredients for 20 people cost £140
Ingredients for 15 people cost   ?

The number of people is in the ratio $\frac{15}{20}$, simplifying to $\frac{3}{4}$.
Therefore the costs are in the same ratio $\frac{3}{4}$.

Therefore the cost of ingredients for 15 people is $\frac{3}{4} \times £140 = £105$.

EXERCISE 3.2

1. A taxi firm buys 2 cars for £24 000. How much would 5 cars cost?

2. A small car used 4 gallons of petrol to travel 200 miles. How far will it travel on 7 gallons of petrol?

---

3. A car uses 6 gallons of petrol to travel 240 miles. How many gallons will be used to travel 180 miles?

4. 5 bottles of beer cost £4.50. How much will 12 bottles cost?

5. A party for 18 people costs £120. How much would the same type of party cost for 24 people? How many people could be invited to the party if the maximum outlay were to be £100?

6. Stair carpet costs £72 for 9 m. How much would 21 m cost?

7. A works canteen allows 500 g of meat for 6 meals. How much meat will be required for 27 meals?

8. A machine tool operator turns out 1200 spindles in a working week of 40 hours. One week, owing to illness he works for only 30 hours. How many spindles did he turn out in that short week?

9. In the workshop a lathe removes 120 g of metal in 8 min. How much will it remove in 12 min?

3.4 Percentages

In Fig. 3.4 the large square is divided into 100 equal, smaller squares. The shaded part consists of 30 smaller squares. The ratio of the shaded section to the whole square is $\frac{30}{100}$. This ratio out of 100 is called *per cent* and written with the symbol %. The symbol % means the number of parts out of 100 parts.

Therefore the shaded part is 30% of the large square.

Fig. 3.4

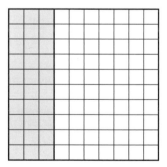

Converting percentages to fractions

(i) Into proper fractions
30% by definition is 30 parts from 100 parts, which can be simplified, that is,

$$\frac{30}{100} = \frac{3}{10}$$

Again 25% is 25 parts out of 100 parts, that is,

$$\frac{25}{100} = \frac{1}{4}$$

(ii) Into decimal fractions

From (i) above $47\% = \frac{47}{100} = 0.47$.

Hence $\qquad 3\% = \frac{3}{100} = 0.03$

$$40\% = 0.40 = 0.4$$

EXAMPLE 3.7

Convert the following percentages into (i) proper fractions and reduce them to the lowest form, (ii) decimal fractions.

$\qquad 10\%, 35\%, 20\%, 5\%, 12\frac{1}{2}\%$

Solution

(i) Converting into proper fractions:

$$10\% = \frac{10}{100} = \frac{1}{10}$$
$$35\% = \frac{35}{100} = \frac{7}{20}$$
$$20\% = \frac{20}{100} = \frac{1}{5}$$
$$5\% = \frac{5}{100} = \frac{1}{20}$$
$$12\frac{1}{2}\% = \frac{12.5}{100} = \frac{1}{8}$$

(ii) Converting into decimal fractions:

$$10\% = 0.1$$
$$35\% = 0.35$$
$$20\% = 0.2$$
$$5\% = 0.05$$
$$12\frac{1}{2}\% = 0.125$$

Converting proper fractions and decimals into percentages

In Fig. 3.5 the shaded part is half the whole square, which is 50 small squares out of 100. This is 50% of the whole square.

$\frac{1}{2} = \frac{50}{100}$ which is defined above as 50%

Therefore a fraction can be converted into a percentage by multiplying the fraction by 100, that is,

$\frac{1}{2}$ becomes $\frac{1}{2} \times 100 = 50\%$

Fig. 3.5

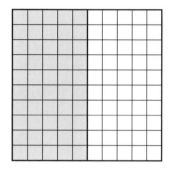

Similarly with decimal fractions

0.312 becomes $0.312 \times 100 = 31.2\%$

EXAMPLE 3.8

Convert the following fractions to percentages:

$\frac{1}{3}$, $\frac{2}{7}$, $\frac{3}{8}$, 0.03, 0.568

Solution

$\frac{1}{3}$ becomes $\frac{1}{3} \times 100$ $= 33\frac{1}{3}\%$

$\frac{2}{7}$ becomes $\frac{2}{7} \times 100$ $= 28\frac{4}{7}\%$

$\frac{3}{8}$ becomes $\frac{3}{8} \times 100$ $= 37.5\%$

0.03 becomes 0.03×100 $= 3\%$

0.568 becomes $0.568 \times 100 = 56.8\%$

The methods of conversion are summarised in Fig. 3.6.

Fig. 3.6

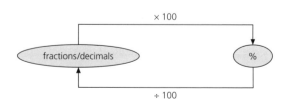

EXAMPLE 3.9

Convert (i) 0.368 to %, (ii) 27% to a decimal fraction.

Solution

(i) Using Fig. 3.6, to convert a decimal fraction to % multiply by 100.

0.368 becomes $0.368 \times 100 = 36.8\%$

(ii) Using Fig. 3.6, to convert a % to a decimal divide by 100.

27% becomes $27 \div 100 = 0.27$

To find a percentage of a number

For example, how much is 20% of 500 packets of sugar?
Writing the percentage as a decimal:

20% of $500 = \frac{20}{100}$ of $500 = 0.2 \times 500 = 100$

EXAMPLE 3.10

A lady wishes to purchase 5 m of material to make curtains. The shopkeeper by mistake cuts a length which is 10% longer. What length did the lady receive?

Solution

Step 1: Additional length is 10% of 5 m $= 0.1 \times 5 \qquad = 0.5$ m

Step 2: Length cut $\qquad\qquad\qquad = 5$ m $+ 0.5$ m $= 5.5$ m

To calculate one number as a percentage of another number

Consider the example where a retailer sells 16 Pentium computers in one week, of which 4 were sold to a college. What percentage was sold to the college?

First, the fraction sold to the college is calculated.

Fraction sold to the college $= \frac{4}{16} \qquad = \frac{1}{4}$

Percentage sold to the college $= \frac{1}{4} \times 100 = 25\%$

EXAMPLE 3.11

A piece of beef weighed 12 kg, but the customer asked for 4 kg to be removed. What percentage did the butcher cut off?

Solution

Fraction of beef cut off = 4 out of 12 kg = $\frac{4}{12}$ = $\frac{1}{3}$

Percentage cut off   = $\frac{1}{3} \times 100$ = $33\frac{1}{3}\%$

EXERCISE 3.3

1. Calculate the following: (i) 20% of 300, (ii) 15% of 20 m, (iii) 8% of 350, (iv) 10% of 400 boxes of matches.

2. Calculate the following as percentages: (i) 10 marks out of 200 in a test, (ii) 15 pints of beer out of 90, (iii) £25 out of £500, (iv) 12 girls in a class of 48.

3. Which of the following is the smallest piece of a whole cake?
   $\frac{5}{9}$, 55%, 0.6

4. A plank of wood is 300 cm long. If 15% was removed, what length was cut off?

5. (i) In the measuring cylinder of liquid shown in Fig. 3.7(a), find the percentage of liquid which has been removed if it originally contained 40 *cl*. (ii) In Fig. 3.7(b), how much liquid will be left if 30% is poured off?

Fig. 3.7

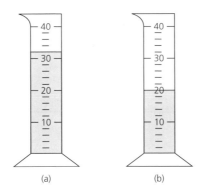

(a)   (b)

6. A dealer is expected to sell 20 cars in a three-month period. However, the franchise contract was increased by a further 15%. How many cars must the dealer now sell?

7. A carton is marked to contain 250 matchboxes. When it was opened it was found to contain only 220 boxes. What was the percentage shortfall?

8. For her engagement party Jill told the hotel that 40 people would attend. When the time came 50 people arrived. What was the percentage increase in the number of people who actually attended?

9. In Fig. 3.8 the shaded part of a beam is to be removed. What percentage of the beam is removed?

Fig. 3.8

10. An engineer was given a specification for an axle to be 40 mm in diameter. However, after making the axle he received a revised specification of 38 mm for the diameter. What % reduction in the diameter did he have to make?

11. A 75 cl bottle of red wine contains 12% of alcohol by volume. How many centi-litres of alcohol does the bottle contain?

12. In a test a student gets a mark of 46 out of a possible total of 78. What was the percentage mark? What mark would be needed in this examination to obtain a pass mark of 40%?

13. A youth club has 80 members. If 60% are girls, how many boys are there in the class?

14. Fig. 3.9 shows a meter for measuring current. The needle moves from B to A. Find the percentage drop in the electric current.

Fig. 3.9

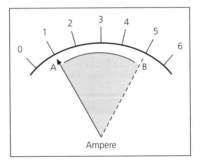

15. A material shrinks by 2% in its first wash. How much would a sleeve, 35 cm long, shrink in the first wash?

16. A drawing which is 200 mm long by 140 mm wide is to be enlarged 30% on a photocopier. What will be the photocopied dimensions?

4 Calculations with money

4.1 Everyday calculations

Addition and subtraction of money

For many years money has been a decimal number with 2 decimal places representing the pence. Thus

22 p = £0.22
6 p = £0.06

Adding and subtracting sums of money becomes the addition and subtraction of decimals. As with all calculations it is important to set out the figures clearly, with the decimal points always in line, as shown in Examples 4.1 and 4.2.

EXAMPLE 4.1

Add together the following sums of money: £15.67, £3.89, £105.06.

Solution

$$
\begin{array}{r}
£15.67 \\
£3.89 \\
\underline{£105.06} \\
\underline{£124.62}
\end{array}
$$

EXAMPLE 4.2

The total for groceries in a supermarket was £52.64, but one item for £6.38 had been counted twice. What was the correct total?

Solution

This is a problem in the subtraction of decimal numbers.

$$
\begin{array}{r}
£52.64 \\
\underline{£\;6.38} \\
\underline{£46.26}
\end{array}
$$

Cost of several items

Shopping involves calculations with money because items are priced singly. Although the totals are now printed out on an invoice from a computer, checking them often means doing the calculations in your head.

A typical calculation is a jar of coffee which costs £1.13, and the cost of 5 jars is required. The calculation becomes the multiplication of a decimal number:

$$£1.13$$
$$\underline{\quad 5}$$
$$£5.65$$

5 jars of coffee will cost £5.65.

When sums of money are multiplied or divided the number of decimal places in the answer will often be more than two, so it is necessary to round off to the nearest penny. Thus £36.784 is rounded to £36.78, and £17.468 is rounded to £17.47 etc., using the rule described in section 2.3.

EXAMPLE 4.3

A metre length of curtain material costs £21.87. How much will a length of 2.5 m cost?

Solution

This is a calculation in long multiplication using the method already shown in section 2.2(b). The decimal point is initially ignored.

$$£2187$$
$$\underline{\quad 25}$$
$$10935$$
$$\underline{43740}$$
$$54675$$

There are a total of 3 decimal places in the original numbers; hence the answer will have 3 decimal places.

Cost of material = £54.675

This is rounded off to the nearest penny. Therefore

Cost of material = £54.68

The price of a single item

If, for example, 8 tins of soup cost £5.76, the cost of a single tin is found by dividing by 8:

$$8 \underline{\mid £5.76}$$
$$£0.72$$

Cost per tin = £0.72 = 72p

EXAMPLE 4.4

2.5 kg of potatoes cost £1.49. What is the cost per kilogram?

Solution

The price per kilogram is £1.49 ÷ 2.5.
The dividing number 2.5 is made a whole number by moving the decimal point 1 place to the right in both numbers, that is 14.9 ÷ 25.

```
        0.596
   25 | 14.900
        12 5
         2 40
         2 25
          150
          150
          . .
```

Price per kilogram = £0.596 = 59.6p
= 60p to the nearest penny

EXERCISE 4.1

1. Three items, purchased in a supermarket, were £1.85, £3.57, £2.19. What was the total price paid and what change would be obtained from a £20 note?

2. Four people had a meal in a restaurant, and the individual meals cost
   £6.40, £8.21, £7.27, £9.36
   What was the total bill? They decided to share the bill. How much did each person pay?

3. In the winter sales a woman purchased the following clothes:
   Dress   £37.99
   Skirt   £24.49
   Blouse   £21.50
   Shoes   £29.99
   How much did she spend altogether?

4. The bill for groceries in a shop was £42.56, but there was a discount of £4.61. What was the actual amount paid to the shopkeeper?

5. The foreman on a production line earns £245.76 a week. From this amount he has deductions of £75.87. How much does he have left?

6. A firm employs 26 people on the production line, and pays each of them £182.65 per week. What is the weekly wages bill for these people?

7. In the market a pot of geraniums costs £3.65. How much will 7 pots cost?

8. A hire firm supplied the following items of crockery for an engagement party:
   25 cups and saucers at £2.20 each
   25 dinner plates at   £1.59 each
   25 small plates at   £1.09 each
   What was the total hire cost?

9. In the office of a car salesroom the following costs were listed for a month:
   Postage   £24.50
   Telephone   £48.25
   Photocopying   £29.00
   Paper   £8.25
   What was the total cost for the month?

10. In a small office, 5 people had monthly salaries of £784 each, 4 people had monthly salaries of £1086, and the office manager earned £1900 per month. Calculate (i) the total monthly salaries bill, (ii) the total annual salaries bill.

4.2 Income

Wages and salaries

For most people the source of their money, called *income*, is the pay they receive from their employers.

When paid weekly the income is called a wage, and it will be based on an hourly rate, such as £5.20 per hour. The total weekly wage will then be

weekly rate × number of hours worked in the week.

An example calculating a weekly wage is shown in Example 4.5.

When paid monthly the income is called a salary, and will be based on an agreed annual sum of money. The monthly salary is then found by dividing the total into 12 equal parts, that is, monthly salary is the

annual salary ÷ 12.

An example is shown in Example 4.6.

EXAMPLE 4.5

The weekly rate for a job on a building site is £5.20 an hour.
If a 40-hour week is worked by a man, what will be his wage for the week?

Solution

Weekly rate   = £5.20
Number of hours   = 40
Wages for the week = £5.20 × 40 = £208

EXAMPLE 4.6

A man's annual income was £16 571. How much did he receive each month?

Solution

Income per month is found by dividing £16 571 by 12.

$$12 \,\lvert\, \underline{£16\,571.00}$$
$$£\ 1\,380.916$$

Income per month, to the nearest penny by rounding off to two places, is £1380.92.

Commission

Another way in which certain people receive income is from commission. These people are mainly in jobs which involve selling, that is, they are sales people. They receive a percentage of the sum of the total sales for a week or a month. This means that their incomes vary from week to week, or month by month. Generally, but not always, they get a basic income, which is then made up with commission, that is

monthly or weekly income = basic income + commission.

A calculation with commission is shown in Example 4.7.

EXAMPLE 4.7

A shop assistant in an electric appliance shop has a basic wage of £110 a week. On top of this she gets 5% commission on all that she sells. One week she sold £730 worth of goods. What was her total wage for that week?

Solution

Basic wage = £110
Commission = 5% of £730 = 0.05 × 730
            = £36.50
Total wages = £110 + £36.50
            = £146.50

Deductions

From the income that everyone gets, two types of deductions are made: (i) National Insurance and (ii) income tax. Income tax is paid by everyone earning over a certain annual sum. These deductions pay for the running of the country, education, the health service and social security. Income tax is based on the annual income. Hence, weekly paid workers have to calculate their total wages for the year, as shown in Example 4.8.

EXAMPLE 4.8

A man receives a weekly wage of £209. How much is this over the year? Over a whole year he pays income tax of £826 and National Insurance contributions of £472. What is the total of his deductions and what is his annual income after deductions?

Solution

Wage for 1 week	£209.00
Wages for 52 weeks	£209.00 × 52
	52
	418 00
	10,450 00
	£10,868.00
Deductions: income tax	£826.00
National Insurance	£472.00
	£1298.00
Annual income after deductions:	£10,868.00
	1,298.00
	£ 9,570.00

1. A man works in a factory for £6.30 per hour. What wage does he get for a 40-hour week?

2. A trainee electrician gets an hourly rate of £4.80. What is his wage for a 38-hour week?

3. A man's wages for 5 weeks were £1569. How much did he receive each week?

4. A trainee in a building firm was paid £9824 a year. What were his wages each week?

5. A waitress in a hotel was paid £3.95 an hour. For a 40-hour week, what wage did she receive?
   A wage of £4.20 per hour was then set by the hotel. How much more does she now earn each week?

6. Shop A pays the assistants £4.50 an hour for a 35-hour week. A second shop B pays the assistants £4.00 per hour for a 40-hour week. Who has the bigger weekly pay?

7. A manager has an annual salary of £18 000. Deductions for the year are £3345. What does he have per month?

8. A sales representative with a cosmetic company gets a basic weekly wage of £120 plus 6% commission of her total sales. In one week she sold £2400 worth of cosmetics. What was her total wage for that week?

9. An insurance salesman worked on a commission-only basis of 8% of sales and premiums paid in any month. One month sales and premiums amounted to £32 450. What was his salary for that month?

10. The cook in a roadside café was paid £4.30 per hour. He worked on average a 40-hour week. What was his average weekly wage?
On his income for a year he had deductions of £1002. What was his annual income after deductions?

4.3 Percentages and money

Many transactions with money involve calculations with percentages, such as interest on deposits in building societies, discounts, profits and loss, depreciation on cars and computers etc.

Calculations to find the percentage of a sum of money

This is the application of percentages, discussed in Chapter 3, to sums of money, such as finding how much, say, 30% of £500 is. Examples of this type of calculation are shown in Example 4.9.

EXAMPLE 4.9

Work out the following:
  (i)   20% of £400
  (ii) 60% of £260
  (iii) 19% of £25
  (iv) $17\frac{1}{2}$% of £300

Solution

  (i)   20% of £400 $= 0.2 \times 400$ $= £80$
  (ii) 60% of £260 $= 0.6 \times 260$ $= £156$
  (iii) 19% of £25 $= 0.19 \times 25$ $= £4.75$
  (iv) $17\frac{1}{2}$% of £300 $= 0.175 \times 300 = £52.50$

Calculations to find one sum of money as a percentage of another

In this type of calculation we find how much, say, £70 is as a percentage of £210. Examples of this type of calculation are shown in Example 4.10.

EXAMPLE 4.10

Find what percentage each sum of money is of the given total in
  (i) £40 from a total of £200
 (ii) £60 from a total of £800
(iii) £10 from a total of £800
(iv) £70 from a total of £400

Solution

  (i) £40 out of £200

Fraction $= \frac{40}{200}$

Percentage $= \frac{40}{200} \times 100 = 20\%$

 (ii) £60 out of £800

Fraction $= \frac{60}{800}$

Percentage $= \frac{60}{800} \times 100 = 7.5\%$

(iii) £10 out of £800

Fraction $= \frac{10}{800}$

Percentage $= \frac{10}{800} \times 100 = 1.25\%$

(iv) £70 out of £400

Fraction $= \frac{70}{400}$

Percentage $= \frac{70}{400} \times 100 = 17.5\%$

Discounts

In the world of commerce, in buying and selling, in shops and mail order, goods are often sold at a discount. This means that the cost to a customer is reduced from the original price. One particular example is the sales period in shops where goods are reduced to clear stock, typically shown in Fig. 4.1 and Example 4.11.

Fig. 4.1

New Year's Sale

All goods will be reduced by
20%
of the marked prices

EXAMPLE 4.11

In the January sales all clothes in a store were reduced by 20%. What is the new price of each of the following items?

Man's suit £110.00
Dress £90.00
Blouse £25.00

Solution

(i) Discount on man's suit = 20% of £110 = 0.2 × 110
                                              = £22
    Sale price   = £110 − £22 = £88

(ii) Discount on dress   = 20% of £90 = 0.2 × 90
                                              = £18
     Sale price   = £90 − £18   = £72

(iii) Discount on blouse   = 20% of £25 = 0.2 × 25
                                              = £5
      Sale price   = £25 − £5   = £20

Profit and loss

In all aspects of commerce, buying and selling involves profit and loss. The manufacturer of cars sells the cars to dealers for a price which is more than the cost of materials and labour, thus making a profit. In the same way the dealer sells the car to a customer at a price which is greater than the price he paid the manufacturer for it, again making a profit.

However, when the customer sells the car after using it for a period, he can only sell it at a price which is less than the price he paid for it, thus making a loss. These profits and losses are usually expressed as percentages.

If a shopkeeper buys a shirt from the manufacturer for £5 and sells it to a customer for £7 then

Profit = £7 − £5 = £2

The profit is now based on the price that the shopkeeper paid for it.

Fractional profit $= \frac{2}{5}$

Percentage profit $= \frac{2}{5} \times 100 = 40\%$

Calculations in profit and loss are shown in Examples 4.12 and 4.13.

EXAMPLE 4.12

A shopkeeper buys a bicycle for £60. He sells it at a profit of £12. What percentage profit does he make?

Solution

Fraction profit of £12 on an outlay of £60 $= \frac{12}{60} = \frac{1}{5}$

Percentage profit $\qquad\qquad\qquad = \frac{1}{5} \times 100 = 20\%$

EXAMPLE 4.13

A store buys a television for £350. The store's policy is to make 40% profit. What is the selling price to a customer?

Solution

$$\text{Profit} = 40\% \text{ of } £350$$
$$= 0.4 \times £350$$
$$= £140$$

$$\text{Price to customer} = £350 + \text{profit}$$
$$= £350 + £140$$
$$= £490$$

Interest

When a person deposits money into any form of savings in a bank or building society he or she will be paid a sum of money by the bank or building society at a predetermined percentage. This sum of money is called the interest and is often paid annually. A calculation is shown in Example 4.14.

EXAMPLE 4.14

A student puts £150 into a high interest account in a building society, paying an annual 6.2% interest. What interest will he receive at the end of the year?

Solution

$$\text{Interest received} = 6.2\% \text{ of } £150$$
$$= 0.062 \times 150$$
$$= £9.30$$

1. Find the following:
   (i) 30% of £200
   (ii) 40% of £270
   (iii) 17% of £76
   (iv) $17\frac{1}{2}$% of £500

2. Find as a percentage of the given total each of the following:
   (i) £40 from a total of £500
   (ii) £60 from a total of £1600
   (iii) £10 from a total of £120
   (iv) £70 from a total of £800

3. A man deposited £250 in a savings account offering an annual interest rate of $6\frac{1}{2}$%. How much interest did he get in one year?

4. Depreciation on a new car was 22% in the first year. If a new car cost £13 000, what was its value after 1 year?

5. The cost of a litre of lead-free petrol was 72p. After a price increase of 3%, what was the new price of a litre?

6. During an evening out to celebrate an engagement, a family paid £108 of which £36 was for drinks. What percentage of the total was the price of the drinks?

7. A firm of accountants paid £13 200 for computers. Depreciation was set at 30%. What were the computers worth after one year?

8. A new car depreciates 18% in the first year. If it cost £14 800 to buy, how much would it be worth after one year?

9. A family paid £640 for a holiday, but because of changes in the rate of exchange they received a rebate of £80. What percentage of the total was the rebate?

10. A businessman deposited £5000 in a building society paying 6% annual interest. How much interest did he receive in one year?

11. A store announced a 20% discount on clothes in the January sales. Find how much a customer would pay for the following goods which were originally marked as shown:
    Dress   £40
    Shoes   £27
    Coat   £80

12. Jack buys a shirt for £12. His girlfriend buys him a designer shirt for £16. How much more did she pay as a percentage?

4.4 Value added tax (VAT)

In this country, as in most other countries, besides income tax, the government charges everybody a value added tax (VAT). This is a tax of $17\frac{1}{2}$% added to the price we pay for some of our goods, such as furniture, electrical equipment, eating out in a restaurant. Food and children's clothes are exempt from VAT. The VAT on electricity and gas costs is 5%.

With VAT at $17\frac{1}{2}\%$ the easiest way to calculate it quickly is to split it up as $10\% + 5\% + 2\frac{1}{2}\%$.

Then calculate 10%, from which 5% is a half and $2\frac{1}{2}\%$ a further half as shown in Example 4.15.

EXAMPLE 4.15

A television costs £200 before VAT. How much is the VAT on the purchase if the rate is $17\frac{1}{2}\%$?

Solution

VAT = 17.5% = 10% of £200 + 5% of £200 + $2\frac{1}{2}\%$ of £200
        = £20 + £10 + £5
        = £35

The alternative way is shown in Examples 4.16 and 4.17.

EXAMPLE 4.16

What is the total price to be paid for a cement mixer which is priced at £160 plus VAT at $17\frac{1}{2}\%$?

Solution

VAT   = $17\frac{1}{2}\%$ of £160 = 0.175 × £160
           = £28.00
Total price = £160 + £28   = £188

EXAMPLE 4.17

What is the VAT on an electricity bill of £160?

Solution

VAT on electricity = 5%
VAT on £160   = 5% of £160
                   = 0.05 × £160
                   = £8

---

1. Find the VAT at $17\frac{1}{2}$% on the following sums of money:
    (i) £40   (ii) £800   (iii) £64   (iv) £150

2. The floor of an office is to be carpeted. The price quoted is £220 plus VAT at $17\frac{1}{2}$%. What is the total cost of the carpet?

3. A household refrigerator was quoted as £180 plus VAT at $17\frac{1}{2}$%. How much would a customer have to pay?

4. The bill for food for 4 people in a restaurant came to £120 plus VAT at $17\frac{1}{2}$%. How much was the total bill, and how much did each person pay if the bill was divided equally between them?

5. A car is marked at £12 000 plus VAT at $17\frac{1}{2}$%. How much would a customer pay for the car?

6. The total cost of telephone calls after any discount is £45. The line rental is £30. If VAT is $17\frac{1}{2}$%, what is the total bill for the quarter?

7. A gas company billed a customer a service charge of £16.40 plus £83.60 for gas used. To this total VAT at 5% was added. What was the customer's total bill?

4.5 Shopping bills

Simple bills are a way of life. Each time we go to the market we get a bill. These bills are lists of goods bought with individual items priced, such as

The Good Shopper

5 kg of carrots	at £0.35/kg	=	£1.75
4 kg of potatoes	at £0.68/kg	=	£2.72
2 kg of grapes	at £0.74/kg	=	£1.48
4 grapefruit	at £0.15 each	=	£0.60
Total			£6.55

Very often the symbol @ is used to denote the price of a single item, so that 5 pineapples at £0.95 each, is written as 5 pineapples @ £0.95.

Another example of a bill is the price of a meal in a restaurant, as shown in Example 4.18.

EXAMPLE 4.18

Three couples went to a restaurant for a meal. At the end of the meal the bill was:

Dine in style

2 main meals at £8.40 each
1 main meal at £10.35 each
3 main meals at £6.20 each
5 desserts at £2.45 each
1 cheese plate at £3.00
5 coffees at £1.20 each
1 bottle of house red wine at £6.25
2 bottles of white wine at £8.00 each

    Total

Calculate the total bill. If the bill was divided equally, calculate what each couple paid.

Solution

The bill was worked out as follows:

Dine in style

2 main meals at £8.40 each	£16.80
1 main meal at £10.35 each	£10.35
3 main meals at £6.20 each	£18.60
5 desserts at £2.45 each	£12.25
1 cheese plate at £3.00	£ 3.00
5 coffees at £1.20 each	£ 6.00
1 bottle of house red wine at £6.25	£ 6.25
2 bottles of white wine at £8.00 each	£16.00
Total	£89.25

Each couple paid   £89.25 ÷ 3 = £29.75

1. The shopping bill in a DIY store was as follows:
   4 cans of paint @ £4.55
   2 packets of Polyfilla @ £1.40
   12 rolls of paper @ £7.39
   4 lengths of wooden rods @ £2.05
   What is the total bill?

2. The items of a meal for four people in a restaurant are shown in the following bill.

   ## Ye Olde Black Swan

   4 starters @ £1.25
   2 main courses @ £8.30
   1 main course @ £11.20
   1 main course @ £6.25
   4 desserts @ £3.30
   4 coffees @ £0.90

   Find the total bill and then calculate the amount paid per head if the bill was divided equally.

3. The following items were purchased in a supermarket:
   5 packs of oranges @ £1.20
   6 boxes of cornflakes @ £0.92
   4 cartons of icecream @ £2.10
   3 packs of butter @ £0.95
   12 tins of soup @ £0.65
   2 kg of apples at £0.85 per kg
   Find the total bill.

4. For a reception to launch a new model of a car a garage bought the following range of drinks:
   6 bottles of red wine @ £5.50
   8 bottles of white wine @ £4.50
   2 bottles of whisky @ £8.75
   2 bottles of gin @ £8.25
   11 bottles of soft drink @ £1.25
   Find the total drinks bill for the reception.

4.6 Rates of exchange of currency

Whenever we go abroad money has to be changed into a different currency, such as

francs (FFr) in France
pesetas (Pta) in Spain
deutschmarks (Dm) in Germany
dollars ($) in the USA

Rates of exchange between different currencies vary day by day.

Exchange rates can be found on Ceefax, on the Internet, in banks and in the newspapers.

The method of converting from one currency to another is shown in Examples 4.19 and 4.20.

EXAMPLE 4.19

The rate of exchange is 9.50 FFr to the pound (£). How many French francs will be obtained for £200?

Solution

£1 will exchange to 9.50 FFr
£200 will exchange to $200 \times 9.50 = 1900$ FFr

After a holiday money has to be changed back to pounds (£). The calculation is shown in Example 4.20.

EXAMPLE 4.20

475 FFr are left over after a holiday. If the rate of exchange is 9.50 FFr to the pound (£), how many pounds will be received back?

Solution

Here the method of proportion can be used to work out the calculation.
Writing out the two statements:

9.50 FFr exchanges to £1
475 FFr exchanges to ?

Ratio of FFr $= \frac{475}{9.5}$

Ratio of £ will be the same $= \frac{475}{9.5}$

Number of pounds (£) $= \frac{475}{9.5} \times £1$

$= £50$

EXAMPLE 4.21

The exchange rate between Spanish pesetas and French francs is 9.90 FFr = 250 Pta. In travelling from Spain to France, how many FFr will be obtained by a tourist for 2000 Pta?

Solution

Using proportion and writing out the two statements:

$\qquad$ 250 Pta = 9.90 FFr
$\qquad$ 2000 Pta = ?

Ratio of Pta $\qquad = \frac{2000}{250} = \frac{8}{1}$

Ratio of FFr will be the same $= \frac{8}{1}$

Number of FFr $\qquad = \frac{8}{1} \times 9.90$

$\qquad\qquad\qquad\qquad = 79.20$ FFr

EXERCISE 4.6

1. How many German Dm will a tourist obtain for £250 if the exchange rate is £1 = 2.95 Dm?

2. An engineer goes to Italy on a project. He wishes to exchange £320 into lire. How many lire will he get if £1 = 2923 L?

3. Returning from Ireland with 480 Irish Punt, a visitor wishes to change them back into pounds (£). How many will he get if £1 = 1.20 IP?

4. A holidaymaker travels from Germany into France, and wishes to change 400 Dm into French francs. How many French francs will he receive when 2.9 Dm = 9.90 FFr?

5. When travelling across the border from Belgium to France a businessman has 8700 BFr. If the exchange rate was 9.50 FFr = 58 BFr how many French francs would he get?

5 Units of measurement

5.1 Introduction

In all aspects of living, at home, at work or at leisure, everyone is required to make or use measurements. Measurements are made of lengths, weight, time, area, capacity, speed etc. In order for everyone to work to the same standards, all quantities must be measured against fixed sizes called *units*.

In the UK two systems of units are used:

(i) the Imperial system
(ii) the metric system

The Imperial system is being replaced by the metric system. During the long transition from Imperial to metric measurement it is necessary to be able to convert measurements from one system to the other.

When numbers refer to measurements, such as length, it is essential to state the unit. This is normally done in shortened form. These are given in the tables that follow.

5.2 Measurement of length in the metric system

In the metric system, most everyday measurements are in metres (m) and centimetres (cm). There are 100 cm in 1 m as shown in Fig. 5.1. Each centimetre is divided into 10 millimetres.

Fig. 5.1

Units for measuring length

Table 5.1 shows the units that are used for measuring length in the metric system. The abbreviated units are shown in brackets.

Smaller or larger units are used for different measurements. The distance between towns will be measured in kilometres; the length of curtain material in metres; the

Table 5.1

Units of length

Kilometre   (km)
Metre   (m)
Centimetre (cm)
Millimetre (mm)

Table 5.2

Relationships

1 km = 1000 m
1 m = 100 cm
1 cm =   10 mm
1 m = 1000 mm

length and width of a sheet of paper in centimetres; the thickness of a glass window pane in millimetres. Because of these various sizes, it is important to be able to convert from one unit to another, using the relationships in Table 5.2.

Changing units

Table 5.2 can be used to change a length in one unit into other units as shown in Example 5.1.

EXAMPLE 5.1

Change   (i) 12 km into metres   (ii) 6.2 m into centimetres
         (iii) 430 cm into metres   (iv) 9 mm into centimetres

Solution

(i)   1 km = 1000 m
       12 km = 1000 × 12 = 12 000 m

(ii)   1 m = 100 cm
        6.2 m = 100 × 6.2 = 620 cm

(iii) 100 cm = 1 m
        1 cm = $\frac{1}{100}$ m
      430 cm = 430 × $\frac{1}{100}$ = 4.30 m

(iv) 10 mm = 1 cm
      1 mm = $\frac{1}{10}$ cm
      9 mm = 9 × $\frac{1}{10}$ = $\frac{9}{10}$ = 0.9 cm

Table 5.2 can also be used to change lengths which have been measured in mixed units, such as 5 cm 9 mm, into a decimal number in one unit only. Therefore, using Example 5.1(iv)

$$5 \text{ cm } 9 \text{ mm} = 5 \text{ cm} + 0.9 \text{ cm} = 5.9 \text{ cm}$$

EXAMPLE 5.2

Write the following lengths as decimal numbers.
(i) 14 cm 9 mm   (ii) 3 m 49 cm   15 km 61 m

Solution

(i) 14 cm 9 mm = 14 cm + 0.9 cm = 14.9 cm

(ii) 3 m 49 cm   = 3 m + $\frac{49}{100}$ m   = 3 + 0.49   = 3.49 m

(iii) 15 km 61 m = 15 km + $\frac{61}{1000}$ km = 15 + 0.061 = 15.061 km

---

EXAMPLE 5.3

Change the following metric units of length.
 (i) 5.3 km to m   (ii) 53 635 m to km   (iii) 0.552 m to cm
(iv) 0.0367 m to mm   (v) 5.48 mm to m

Solution

Using the metric conversion shown in Table 5.2:

(i)   1 km = 1000 m
          5.3 km = 1000 × 5.3   = 5300 m

(ii)   1000 m = 1 km
            1 m = $\frac{1}{1000}$ km
          53 635 m = 53 635 × $\frac{1}{1000}$ = 53.635 km

(iii)   1 m = 100 cm
          0.552 m = 100 × 0.552   = 55.2 cm

(iv)   1 m = 1000 mm
          0.0367 m = 1000 × 0.0367 = 36.7 mm

(v)   1000 mm = 1 m
            1 mm = $\frac{1}{1000}$ m
          5.48 mm = 5.48 × $\frac{1}{1000}$ = 0.00548 m

To find the number of smaller lengths in a larger length

The number of smaller lengths in a larger one is found by dividing the smaller one into the larger one. However, before doing so both lengths must be in the same units, that is, both metres, or feet, or millimetres. The best units to use are those of the smaller length as shown in Example 5.4.

EXAMPLE 5.4

Find the number of 6 cm pieces that can be cut from a steel rod 1.54 m long. What is the length of the piece left over?

Solution

Both lengths must be in the same units, which in this case is centimetres.

$$\text{Length of steel rod} = 1.54 \text{ m} = 1.54 \times 100 = 154 \text{ cm}$$
$$\text{Length of pieces to be cut} = 6 \text{ cm}$$
$$\text{Number of pieces} = 154 \div 6$$
$$= 6 \underline{| \ 154}$$
$$\underline{25} \text{ remainder } 4$$

$$\text{Number of pieces} = 25$$
$$\text{Length of piece left over} = 4 \text{ cm}$$

EXERCISE 5.1

1. What are the most appropriate units to measure the following?
   Length of a table
   Length of a football pitch
   Thickness of a wall tile
   Thickness of sheet of paper
   Width of a TV screen
   Distance from London to Scotland
   Height of a door
   Width of a wall tile
   Height of a house
   Length of a garden path

2. Change the following lengths:
   (i) 12.5 km into m   (ii) 0.0563 km into cm
   (iii) 0.00861 km into mm   (iv) 14.36 m into cm

---

3. Change the following metric units of length:
    (i) 12.1 m into mm   (ii) 4.61 m into cm   (iii) 450 cm into m
    (iv) 32.5 cm into m   (v) 390 mm into m   (vi) 41 000 mm into m

4. A steel rod is 1.26 m long. How many pieces 6 cm long can be cut from it?

5. A wooden batten is 1.2 m long. How many pieces, 125 mm long, can be cut from it? What is the length of the remaining piece if each saw cut is 2 mm wide?

6. A copper pipe for central heating is 3 m long. Three pieces, 132.2 cm, 98.0 cm and 69.5 cm long are required to fit a radiator in a room. Can the three pieces be obtained from this single length if each cut of the pipe is 1 mm wide?

7. The height of a window was measured as 1350 mm. A curtain was required to hang 250 mm below the bottom of the window. To allow for binding etc. a further 200 mm was required. The shopkeeper cut a length of 2 m. What length of material was spare?

Estimating distances

In order to get an understanding of lengths and distances it is a useful practice to make estimations. Reasonable estimates can be obtained by comparing them with an object whose length is known approximately, such as a person's height, finger length, width of a car. This is shown below:

(a) The height of a man is usually less than 2 m but we can use this height to estimate that the
    height of a door is about 2 m
    height to a ceiling is about 2.5 m
    length of a car is about 3 m.

(b) The length of a dinner knife is about 20 cm. Therefore this length can be used to estimate that the
    diameter of a dinner plate is about 25 cm
    diameter of a medium-size saucepan is 20 cm
    internal width of an oven is about 40 cm
    diameter of a jug is about 10 cm.

(c) The thickness of a penny is about 1 mm. Therefore this thickness can be used to estimate that the
    thickness of a floppy disk for a computer is about 3 mm
    thickness of a cheque book is about 5 mm
    thickness of an envelope is about 1 mm
    thickness of 100 sheets of computer paper is about 10 mm.

EXERCISE 5.2

1. By making a comparison with a known object, estimate
    (i) the width of a medium-size car
    (ii) the width of a lane of the motorway

    (iii) the width of a 3-lane motorway including the hard shoulder

    (iv) the height of a two-storey house

    (v) the width of a typical supermarket trolley

    (vi) the diameter of a wheel of a bicycle

    (vii) the height of an adult chair

    (viii) the height of a table

    (ix) the diameter of microbore copper pipe used in central heating.

2. Which of the following statements must be incorrect?

    (i) The length of a desk is 7.2 m.

    (ii) The height of a garden shed is 198 cm.

    (iii) The diameter of a hosepipe is 63 mm.

    (iv) The thickness of aluminium cooking foil is 0.5 mm.

5.3 Measurement of weight in the metric system

Units of weight

Table 5.3 shows the units of weight in the metric system used every day, with the relationships between them listed in Table 5.4.

Table 5.3

Units of weight

Tonne   (t)
Kilogram (kg)
Gram   (g)
Milligram (mg)

Table 5.4

Relationships

1 t = 1000 kg
1 kg = 1000 g
1 g = 1000 mg

As in the case of measuring distances, smaller or larger units are used in different circumstances. Hardcore for motorways is measured in tonnes; bags of potatoes in kilograms; ingredients for cooking in grams; drugs in medicines in milligrams. Because of these various sizes, it is important to be able to convert from one unit to another, using the relationships in Table 5.4, as shown in Example 5.5.

EXAMPLE 5.5

Change the following metric units of weight:
  (i) 5 kg into g   (ii) 6 t into kg   (iii) 956 kg into t
  (iv) 361 g into kg   (v) 4.37 g into mg   (vi) 0.00671 kg into mg

Solution

(i)   1 kg = 1000 g
         5 kg = 5 × 1000 = 5000 g

(ii)   1 t = 1000 kg
          6 t = 6 × 1000 = 6000 kg

(iii)   1000 kg = 1 t
          1 kg = $\frac{1}{1000}$ t
          956 kg = 956 × $\frac{1}{1000}$ = 0.956 t

(iv)   1000 g = 1 kg
          1 g = $\frac{1}{1000}$ kg
          361 g = 361 × $\frac{1}{1000}$ = 0.361 kg

(v)   1 g = 1000 mg
          4.37 g = 4.37 × 1000 = 4370 mg

(vi)   1 kg = 1000 g
               = 1000 × 1000 mg
          0.00671 kg = 0.00671 × 1000 × 1000 = 6710 mg

To find the number of smaller weights in a larger weight

The number of smaller weights in a larger weight is found by dividing the smaller one into the larger one. Both numbers, however, must be in the same units. The best units to use are those of the smaller weight, as shown in Example 5.6.

EXAMPLE 5.6

A jar contains 4 kg of sweets. How many packets of 125 g can be sold from the whole jar?

Solution

Convert both weights into grams:
Weight of sweets in the jar = 4 kg = 4 × 1000 g = 4000 g
    Weight of each packet = 125 g
        Number of packets = 4000 ÷ 125 = 32

1. In what units would you measure the weights of the following?
   A man
   A lorry load of chippings
   A bag of potatoes
   Ingredients for a cake
   A dental filling for a tooth

2. Change the following metric units of weight:
   (i) 11.24 t to kg
   (ii) 0.00056 t to kg
   (iii) 27 560 kg to t
   (iv) 0.92 kg to g
   (v) 0.00446 kg to g
   (vi) 72 950 g to kg
   (vii) 4.97 g to mg
   (viii) 0.00513 kg to mg
   (ix) 79 187 mg to g

3. A carton of cornflakes weighs 1.0 kg. How many 20 g portions can be obtained from the carton?

4. A lady in a slimming class weighs 80 kg. Over a period of 20 weeks she wishes to lose weight until she is 60 kg. How much should she aim to lose (i) each week, (ii) each day? Express your answer in grams.

5. In a fish and chip shop 40 kg of potatoes are fried each day. If 2 t of potatoes are delivered at a time, how many days' supply is this?

6. A chef purchases a joint of meat weighing 25 kg. 40% is lost in trimming and cooking. How much meat is available for serving? How many 125 g portions can be obtained from it?

7. A steel weight is required to be manufactured to be precisely 0.21 kg. After machining the weight was found to be 0.225 kg. How much more metal needs to be removed? Express your answer in milligrams.

5.4 The measurement of area

Table 5.5 shows the units used for measuring area in the metric system, with the relationships between them shown in Table 5.6. Since area is found by multiplying a length by a length, such as metre by metre, its unit is written as m^2 etc., using the methods of indices shown in chapter 1.

The conversion from m^2 to cm^2 is illustrated in Fig. 5.2, where both squares have the same area.

Table 5.5

Units of area

Square kilometre (km²)
Hectare (ha)
Square metre (m²)
Square centimetre (cm²)
Square millimetre (mm²)

Table 5.6

Relationships

1 km² = 1000 m × 1000 m = 1 000 000 m²
1 ha = 100 m × 100 m   = 10 000 m²
1 km²   = 100 ha
1 m² = 100 cm × 100 cm = 10 000 cm²
1 cm² = 10 mm × 10 mm   = 100 mm²

Fig. 5.2

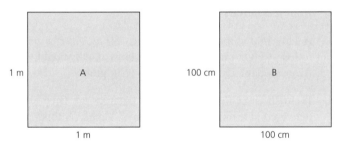

Area of square A = 1 m × 1 m   = 1 m²
Area of square B = 100 cm × 100 cm = 10 000 cm²
Therefore   1 m² = 10 000 cm²

Table 5.6 is used to convert from one unit to another as shown in Example 5.7.

EXAMPLE 5.7

Convert the following:
(i) 5 ha to m²   (ii) 3.5 m² to cm²   (iii) 5400 cm² to m²

Solution

(i)   Using the above conversion table
          1 ha = 10 000 m²
          5 ha = 5 × 10 000 = 50 000 m²

(ii)
$$1 \text{ m}^2 = 10\ 000 \text{ cm}^2$$
$$3.5 \text{ m}^2 = 3.5 \times 10\ 000 \text{ cm}^2 = 35\ 000 \text{ cm}^2$$

(iii) $10\ 000 \text{ cm}^2 = 1 \text{ m}^2$
$$1 \text{ cm}^2 = \tfrac{1}{10\ 000} \text{ m}^2$$
$$5400 \text{ cm}^2 = \tfrac{1}{10\ 000} \times 5400 = 0.54 \text{ m}^2$$

EXERCISE 5.4

1. The area of a piece of common ground is 3.67 km². What is this area in (i) hectares (ii) m²?

2. A table top has an area of 6 m². What is this area in cm²?

3. The surface of a computer screen has an area of 3600 cm². Express this in m².

4. The area of tin plate required to make a soup can is 353 cm². What is this in mm²?

5. A patio has an area of 2 100 000 mm². Express this in m².

5.5 Measurement of capacity (volume) in the metric system

Units of capacity

Capacity is the space confined within a definite boundary such as the space inside a petrol tank of a car, or the space inside a medicine bottle. Table 5.7 shows the units used for measuring capacity in the metric system and Table 5.8 gives the relationships between these units.

Table 5.7

Units of capacity

Cubic metre	(m³)
Litre	(*l*)
Centilitre	(c*l*)
Millilitre	(m*l*)
Cubic centimetre	(cm³)

Note: 1 m*l* is the same size as 1 cm³ but millilitres are generally used for the capacity of liquids.

Relationships
___

$1 \text{ m}^3 = 1000 \ l$
$1 \ l \quad = 1000 \text{ m}l \text{ or cm}^3$
$1 \ l \quad = 100 \text{ c}l$
$1 \text{ c}l = 10 \text{ m}l$

Different units of capacity will be applicable in different situations, such as the volume of concrete in cubic metres; the volume of central heating oil in litres; the capacity of a wine bottle in centilitres; the capacity of medicine bottles in millilitres. Because of these various sizes, it is important to be able to convert from one unit to another, using the relationships in Table 5.8. Conversions between the various metric units of capacity are shown in Example 5.8.

EXAMPLE 5.8

Change the following metric units of capacity:
  (i) 4.5 m³ to l (ii) 0.003617 m³ to l (iii) 44 160 l to m³
  (iv) 1.2 l to cl (v) 0.56 l to ml (vi) 700 ml to l
 (vii) 0.17 l to cm³

Solution

    (i) $1 \text{ m}^3 = 1000 \ l$
           $4.5 \text{ m}^3 = 4.5 \times 1000 \ l = 4500 \ l$

    (ii) $1 \text{ m}^3 = 1000 \ l$
     $0.003617 \text{ m}^3 = 0.003617 \times 1000 = 3.617 \ l$

    (iii) $1000 \ l = 1 \text{ m}^3$
           $1 \ l = \frac{1}{1000} \text{ m}^3$
     $44 \ 160 \ l = 44 \ 160 \times \frac{1}{1000} = 44.16 \text{ m}^3$

    (iv) $1 \ l = 100 \text{ c}l$
       $1.2 \ l = 120 \text{ c}l$

    (v) $1 \ l = 1000 \text{ m}l$
     $0.56 \ l = 560 \text{ m}l$

    (vi) $1000 \text{ m}l = 1 \ l$
        $1 \text{ m}l = \frac{1}{1000} \ l$
     $700 \text{ m}l = 700 \times \frac{1}{1000} \ l = 0.7 \ l$

    (vii) $1 \ l = 1000 \text{ cm}^3$
     $0.17 \ l = 1000 \times 0.17 \text{ cm}^3 = 170 \text{ cm}^3$

To find how many smaller volumes can be obtained from a larger volume

The number of smaller volumes can be found by dividing one into the other, as shown in Example 5.9, having first brought both quantities to the same units. The best units to use are those of the smaller volume.

EXAMPLE 5.9

A vat contains 1.5 m³ of fermented wine. How many 75 *cl* bottles can be filled from it?

Solution

Bringing both quantities to *cl*

$$\text{Capacity of the vat} = 1.5 \text{ m}^3$$
$$= 1.5 \times 1000 \; l$$
$$= 1.5 \times 1000 \times 100 \; cl$$
$$\text{Capacity of the wine bottles} = 75 \; cl$$
$$\text{Number of bottles} = 1.5 \times 1000 \times 100 \div 75$$
$$= 2000$$

EXERCISE 5.5

1. What metric units would be appropriate to express the capacity of the following?
   Petrol tank of a car
   An oil tanker
   A bottle of beer
   A bottle of eye drops
   A water reservoir
   A can of engine oil
   A syringe

2. Change the following metric units of capacity:
   (i) 2.2 m³ to *l*   (ii) 0.0056 m³ to m*l*   (iii) 4 330 000 m*l* to m³
   (iv) 20 *l* to *cl*   (v) 0.0067 *l* to m*l*   (vi) 60 *cl* to m*l*
   (vii) 1240 cm³ to *l*

3. How many 5 m*l* spoonfuls can be obtained from a $\frac{1}{4}$ *l* of medicine?

4. A bottle of wine contains 75 *cl* of wine. A glass of wine will contain approximately 125 m*l*. How many glasses of wine can you obtain from the bottle?

5. A liquid weedkiller is sold in 50 m*l* bottles. It needs diluting with water in the ratio 2.5 m*l* to 2 *l*. How many litres of diluted weedkiller will a bottle produce?

5.6 Imperial measuring system

The units of measurement used until recently in the UK are shown in Table 5.9. Table 5.10 is used to convert from one Imperial unit to another. However, whereas the conversions in metric always involve multiples of 10, in Imperial units the numbers are more complicated. Changing Imperial units is demonstrated in Example 5.10.

Table 5.9

Units of length	Units of weight	Units of capacity
Mile	Ton	Gallon (gal)
Yard (yd)	Pound (lb)	Pint (pt)
Foot (ft)	Ounce (oz)	Fluid ounce (fl oz)
Inch (in)		

Table 5.10

Relationships

1 mile = 1760 yd	1 ton = 2240 lb	1 gal = 8 pt
1 yd = 3 ft	1 lb = 16 oz	1 pt = 20 fl oz
1 ft = 12 in		

EXAMPLE 5.10

Using Table 5.10 change the following Imperial units:
  (i) 2 miles to yd   (ii) 3 ft to in   (iii) 48 oz to lb
  (iv) 3 ton to lb   (v) 6 pints to fl oz   (vi) 30 pints to gal

Solution

(i) $1 \text{ mile} = 1760 \text{ yd}$
            $2 \text{ miles} = 2 \times 1760 = 2520 \text{ yd}$

(ii) $1 \text{ ft} = 12 \text{ in}$
            $3 \text{ ft} = 3 \times 12 \quad = 36 \text{ in}$

(iii) $16 \text{ oz} = 1 \text{ lb}$
    Therefore $1 \text{ oz} = \frac{1}{16} \text{ lb}$
            $48 \text{ oz} = \frac{1}{16} \times 48 \quad = 3 \text{ lb}$

(iv) $1 \text{ ton} = 2240 \text{ lb}$
            $3 \text{ ton} = 3 \times 2240 = 6720 \text{ lb}$

(v)	1 pt = 20 fl oz
	6 pt = 6 × 20 = 120 fl oz
(vi)	8 pt = 1 gal
	1 pt = $\frac{1}{8}$ gal
	30 pt = 30 × $\frac{1}{8}$ = $3\frac{3}{4}$ gal

5.7 Conversion between metric and Imperial systems

Table 5.11 shows the conversions between Imperial and metric units of length, weight and capacity.

Table 5.11

Length	
Imperial → Metric	*Metric → Imperial*
1 mile = 1.61 km	1 km = 0.621 mile
1 ft = 0.305 m	1 m = 3.28 ft
1 in = 25.4 mm	1 mm = 0.0394 in

Weight	
Imperial → Metric	*Metric → Imperial*
1 ton = 1.02 t	1 t = 0.984 ton
1 lb = 0.454 kg	1 kg = 2.20 lb
1 oz = 28.4 g	1 g = 0.0353 oz

Capacity	
Imperial → Metric	*Metric → Imperial*
1 gal = 4.55 *l*	1 *l* = 0.220 gal
1 pt = 0.568 *l*	1 *l* = 1.76 pt
1 fl oz = 28.4 m*l*	1 m*l* = 0.0352 fl oz

To construct a table for converting (i) feet to metres and (ii) metres to feet

For routine work conversions can be made using tables as shown in Example 5.11. Tables can be constructed such as Table 5.11. The conversions are correct to 3 significant figures.

(i) Converting from feet to metres

From Table 5.11 we have:

    1 ft = 0.305 m
    2 ft = 0.305 × 2 = 0.610 m
    3 ft = 0.305 × 3 = 0.915 m

The conversions up to 9 ft are shown in Table 5.12(a).

(ii) Converting from metres to feet

From Table 5.11 we have:

    1 m = 3.28 ft
    2 m = 2 × 3.28 = 6.56 ft
    3 m = 3 × 3.28 = 9.84 ft

The conversions up to 9 m are shown in Table 5.12(b).

Table 5.12

Feet → Metre		Metre → Feet	
1	0.305	1	3.28
2	0.610	2	6.56
3	0.915	3	9.84
4	1.22	4	13.1
5	1.53	5	16.4
6	1.83	6	19.7
7	2.14	7	23.0
8	2.44	8	26.2
9	2.75	9	29.5

        (a)   (b)

From the table we can find the conversion between feet and metres for other values as shown in Example 5.11.

EXAMPLE 5.11

Using Table 5.11 convert the following lengths:
  (i) 0.1 m to ft   (ii) 0.03 m to ft   (iii) 40 m to ft
(iv) 3.46 m to ft   (v) 0.7 ft to m   (vi) 27.1 ft to m

Solution

  (i) From the table   1 m = 3.28 ft
        Therefore   0.1 m = 3.28 ÷ 10 = 0.328 ft

(ii)	$3\ m = 9.84\ ft$
	$0.03\ m = 9.84 \div 100 = 0.0984\ ft$
(iii)	$4\ m = 13.1\ ft$
	$40\ m = 13.1 \times 10 = 131\ ft$
(iv)	$3.46\ m = 3\ m \quad + 0.4\ m\ + 0.06\ m$
	$= 9.84\ ft + 1.31\ ft + 0.197\ ft$
	$= 11.347\ ft$

Therefore $3.46\ m = 11.3\ ft$ correct to 3 significant figures

(v)	$7\ ft = 2.14\ m$
	$0.7\ ft = 2.14 \div 10 = 0.214\ m$
(vi)	$27.1\ ft = 20\ ft \quad + 7\ ft \quad + 0.1\ ft$
	$= 6.10\ m + 2.14\ m + 0.0305\ m$
	$= 8.2705\ m$
	$= 8.27\ m$

EXERCISE 5.6

1. Using the same method as above, produce conversion tables correct to 3 significant figures for
   (a) (i) millimetres into inches
        (ii) kilometres into miles
   (b) (i) kilograms into pounds
        (ii) grams into ounces
   (c) (i) gallons into litres
        (ii) pints into litres
        (iii) millilitres into fluid ounces

2. Using tables convert the following:
   (i) 3.45 in to mm   (ii) 25 lb to kg   (iii) 45.6 m*l* to fl oz
   (iv) 2.7 oz to g   (v) 24.3 *l* to pt

3. A man buys 12 gallons of petrol. What is this in litres?

4. Central heating copper pipe in Imperial measurement was a $\frac{1}{2}$ inch in diameter. When metric measurements were introduced the nearest size was 12 mm. Find the percentage difference of the metric size to the Imperial size.

5. A cookery recipe gives a liquid measure as 4 fl oz. What is this in m*l*?

6. A lorry has a load limit of 24 tons. If its actual load is 24 tonnes, by how much is it within its limit or overloaded?

7. The distance between two towns is 40 miles. What is this distance in kilometres?

8. A person is 6 ft 3 in tall. What is this height in metres?

9. Two boys weigh respectively 42 kg and 87 lb. Which boy is the heavier and by how many kilograms?

5.8 Approximate conversions

It is often useful to be able to make approximate conversions between metric and Imperial units. The list below consists of some of the more useful ones, which can be obtained from Table 5.11 by rounding figures to convenient values.

1 mile is approximately 1.5 km
1 in   is approximately 2.5 cm or 25 mm
1 ft   is approximately 30 cm
1 yd   is approximately 1 m
1 ton is approximately 1 t
1 kg   is approximately 2 lb
1 oz   is approximately 25 g
1 gal is approximately 4.5 l
1 l is approximately 2 pt
1 fl oz is approximately 25 ml

EXERCISE 5.7

Use the approximate conversions in the following questions:
1. (i) 6 miles to km   (ii) 2 ft 6 in to cm   (iii) 10 kg to lb
    (iv) 200 mm to in   (v) 9 lb to kg   (vi) 2 in to mm
    (vii) 12 yd to m   (viii) 3 gal to l (ix) 7 tons to t
    (x) 3 ft to cm

2. The top of a jewellery box is 10 in by 6 in. What is the approximate length and breadth in centimetres?

3. A bag of potatoes weighs 25 kg. What is the approximate weight in pounds?

4. The following ingredients are part of a recipe:
    Topside of beef $1\frac{1}{2}$ lb
    Flour   2 oz
    Fat   5 oz
    Sliced onions   12 oz
    Tomato puree   3 oz
    Water   4 fl oz
    Write the recipe in metric units using the approximate conversions.

5. An oil tank has the capacity to hold 500 gal of heating oil. How many litres will the tank hold?

5.9 The measurement of temperature

The two main scales of measurement used in the UK are Fahrenheit and Celsius, although Fahrenheit is being phased out, with most measurements now being carried out in Celsius. The units are degree Celsius (°C) and degree Fahrenheit (°F). The scales are shown in Fig. 5.3.

Fig. 5.3

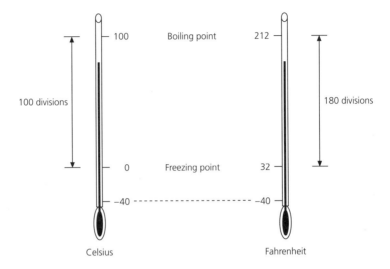

Between the freezing point and the boiling point of water

    the Celsius scale is divided into 100 divisions
    the Fahrenheit scale is divided into 180 divisions

as shown in Fig. 5.3.
    Therefore

           100 divisions C   is equivalent to   180 divisions F
    or   5 divisions C   is equivalent to   9 divisions F

To convert from one scale to another we can use the fact that −40° on the Celsius scale is the same value −40° on the Fahrenheit scale, as shown in Fig. 5.3. Converting from one scale to another can be carried out by referring any value of the temperature to −40°.

Converting Celsius to Fahrenheit

(i)   Add 40 to the Celsius temperature to give the number of divisions above −40°.
(ii)   Multiply by $\frac{9}{5}$.
(iii) Subtract 40 to give the number of divisions above 0 °F which is the Fahrenheit temperature.

The conversion is shown in Example 5.12.

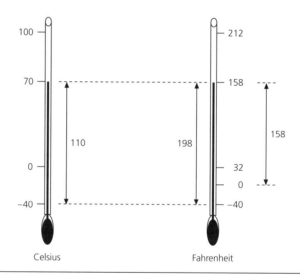

EXAMPLE 5.12

Convert 70 °C to Fahrenheit.

Solution

   (i) Add 40   : 70 + 40 = 110

  (ii) Multiply by $\frac{9}{5}$: 110 × $\frac{9}{5}$ = 198

 (iii) Subtract 40   : 198 − 40 = 158

Therefore   70 °C = 158 °F

The method is illustrated in Fig. 5.4.

Fig. 5.4

Celsius   Fahrenheit

Converting Fahrenheit to Celsius

   (i)   Add 40 to the Fahrenheit temperature to give the number of divisions above −40°.

  (ii) Multiply by $\frac{5}{9}$.

 (iii) Subtract 40 to give the number of divisions above 0 °C, which is the Celsius temperature.

The conversion is shown in Example 5.13.

EXAMPLE 5.13

Convert 77 °F to Celsius.

Solution

(i)   Add 40 : 77 + 40 = 117

(ii) Multiply by $\frac{5}{9}$: 117 × $\frac{5}{9}$ = 65

(iii)   Subtract 40 : 65 − 40 = 25

Therefore   77 °F   = 25 °C

The method is shown in Fig. 5.5.

Fig. 5.5

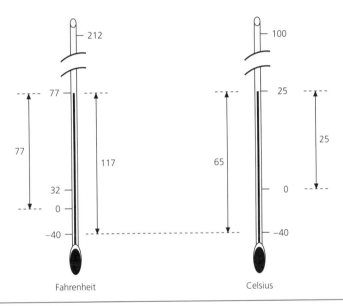

EXERCISE 5.8

1. Convert the following temperatures from Fahrenheit to Celsius:
    182°,   74°,   33°,   −20°,   −60°

2. Convert the following temperatures from Celsius to Fahrenheit:
    41°,   4°,   −23°,   −58°

3. The weather forecast on TV listed the temperatures one day as
    Scotland   6 °C
    Midlands   10 °C
    South of England   14 °C
    Wales   12 °C

    Convert these temperatures to Fahrenheit.

6 Areas and volumes I

6.1 Introduction to areas and perimeters

Area is the amount of surface contained within a boundary. The length of the boundary enclosing the area is called the perimeter (Fig. 6.1).

Fig. 6.1

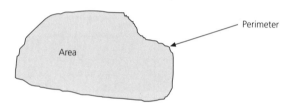

Area

Perimeter

Unit of area

The unit of area in the metric system is a square 1 m by 1 m called a square metre (written as 1 m²).

The unit of area in the Imperial system is a square 1 ft × 1 ft called a square foot (written as 1 ft²).

These are shown in Fig. 6.2.

Fig. 6.2

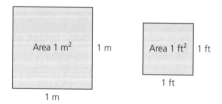

Area 1 m²   1 m

Area 1 ft²   1 ft

1 m

1 ft

Unit of perimeter

Since the perimeter is the length around a boundary it is measured in metres or feet.

6.2 Area and perimeter of a rectangle

Consider a rectangle shown in Fig. 6.3 which is 4 m by 3 m. It can be divided up into squares 1 m by 1 m making 12 squares, so that

$$\text{area} = 12 \text{ m}^2$$

Fig. 6.3

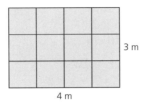

3 m

4 m

It can be seen therefore that the area of a rectangle can be found by multiplying the length by the width, that is 4 m × 3 m = 12 m².

The perimeter is the sum of the lengths of the four sides

$$= 4 + 3 + 4 + 3 = 14 \text{ m}$$

It can be seen that the perimeter is length + length + width + width that is, 2 × length + 2 × width.

These results can be used for any rectangle of length L and with W as shown in Fig. 6.4.

Fig. 6.4

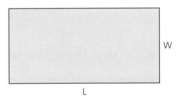

W

L

Therefore

$$\text{Area} = \text{Length} \times \text{Width}$$

RULE

$A = L \times W$

$$\text{Perimeter} = 2 \times \text{Length} + 2 \times \text{Width}$$

RULE

$P = 2L + 2W$

To use the above formulae L and W must be in the same units, that is, both in metres or both in feet, etc., as shown in Example 6.1.

Find the area and perimeter of a rectangle whose length is 5 cm and width is 2 cm.

Solution

$$\text{Area of rectangle} = L \times W$$
$$= 5 \times 2$$
$$= 10 \text{ cm}^2$$
$$\text{Perimeter} = 2L + 2W$$
$$= 2 \times 5 + 2 \times 2$$
$$= 14 \text{ cm}$$

This formula can be used when the sides are not in whole numbers as shown in Example 6.2.

Find the area and perimeter of a rectangle 3.5 m long and 2.2 m wide.

Solution

$$\text{Area} = L \times W$$
$$= 3.5 \times 2.2$$
$$= 7.7 \text{ m}^2 \quad \text{to two significant figures}$$
$$\text{Perimeter} = 3.5 + 2.2 + 3.5 + 2.2$$
$$= 11.4 \text{ m}$$

6.3 Area and perimeter of a square

Fig. 6.5

A square, shown in Fig. 6.5, is a special case of a rectangle, when the length and the width are equal. Therefore

$$\text{Area} = L \times L \qquad = L^2$$
$$\text{Perimeter} = L + L + L + L = 4L$$

EXAMPLE 6.3

Find the area and perimeter of a square of sides 1.7 m long.

Solution

$$\text{Area} = L^2 = 1.7^2$$
$$= 2.89 \text{ m}^2$$
$$= 2.9 \text{ m}^2 \quad \text{to 2 significant figures}$$

Perimeter $= 4L = 4 \times 1.7 = 6.8$ m

6.4 Compound areas

A more complicated area can be calculated by dividing it up into rectangles, as shown in Example 6.4.

EXAMPLE 6.4

A garden is shown in Fig. 6.6. Calculate its area.

Fig. 6.6

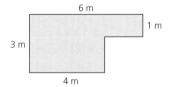

Solution

The calculation can be carried out by dividing the garden layout into two rectangles X and Y, as shown in Fig. 6.7.

Fig. 6.7

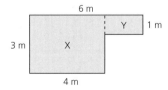

Area of rectangle $X = L \times W \quad$ where $L = 4$ m, $W = 3$ m
$$= 4 \times 3$$
$$= 12 \text{ m}^2$$

Area of rectangle Y = L × W   where L = (6 − 4) = 2 m, W = 1 m
$$= 2 \times 1$$
$$= 2 \text{ m}^2$$

Total area = 12 + 2 = 14 m²
Perimeter = 3 + 6 + 1 + 2 + 2 + 4
$$= 18 \text{ m}$$

EXAMPLE 6.5

Fig. 6.8 shows a garden with a lawn surrounded by a path 1 m wide. Calculate the area of the path.

Fig. 6.8

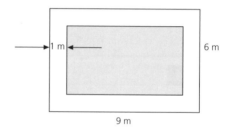

9 m

Solution

Since the path is 1 m wide

Length of the lawn is 9 − 2 = 7 m
Width of the lawn is 6 − 2 = 4 m

The area of the path can be found by subtracting the area of the lawn from the total area.

Total area = L × W
$$= 9 \times 6 \quad = 54 \text{ m}^2$$
Area of the lawn = L × W
$$= 7 \times 4 \quad = 28 \text{ m}^2$$
Area of path = 54 − 28 = 26 m²

6.5 Floor and wall coverings

A job that occurs at home or at work is to find how much paint is needed to cover a wall, the number of tiles to cover a wall or the number of carpet squares to cover a floor. Such a problem is worked out in Examples 6.6 and 6.7.

EXAMPLE 6.6

A wall of a building which is 12 m by 8 m is to be painted. A tin of paint specifies that it will cover an area of 10 m². Calculate how many tins will be needed.

Solution

$$\text{Area of wall} = 12 \times 8 \ = 96 \text{ m}^2$$
$$\text{Area covered by 1 tin} = 10 \text{ m}^2$$
$$\text{Number of tins} = 96 \div 10 = 9.6$$

which means that 10 tins have to be purchased.

The method of dividing areas used in Example 6.6 cannot be used to decide how many tiles can fit into a given area unless they fit exactly. The calculation can be carried out in an alternative way by finding how many tiles will fit along the length and then how many rows of tiles will fit along the width, as shown in Example 6.7.

EXAMPLE 6.7

The floor of a room is 4 m by 3 m. It is to be covered with carpet squares $\frac{1}{2}$ m by $\frac{1}{2}$ m. Find how many carpet squares are required to cover the whole floor.

Solution

Fig. 6.9 shows a diagram of the floor and the carpet square.

Fig. 6.9

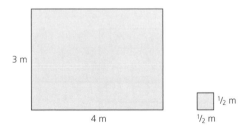

To find the number of squares that can be placed along the 4 m length we find how many $\frac{1}{2}$ m lengths there are in 4 m, that is,

$$\text{Number of squares along the 4 m length} = 4 \div \tfrac{1}{2} = 8$$
Similarly the number of rows that will fit along the 3 m width $= 3 \div \tfrac{1}{2} = 6$

This is shown in Fig. 6.10.

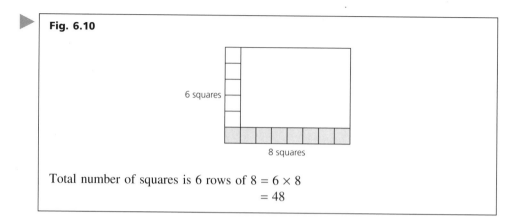

Fig. 6.10

6 squares

8 squares

Total number of squares is 6 rows of 8 = 6×8
$$= 48$$

1. Find the areas and perimeters of the rectangles.
   (i) 8 m × 4 m   (ii) 4 ft × 2.5 ft   (iii) $\frac{1}{8}$ m × $\frac{4}{5}$ m   (iv) 3.6 cm × 2.7 cm

2. Calculate the shaded areas in Fig. 6.11.

Fig. 6.11

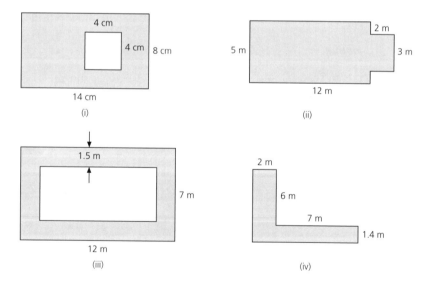

3. A coffee table top is 60 cm long and 20 cm wide. It is to be covered by veneer squares 4 cm by 4 cm. How many veneer squares will be required?

4. A wall of a bathroom, 8 ft by 12 ft, is to be tiled. The tiles are 6 in by 6 in. How many tiles will be required to cover the wall?

Fig. 6.12

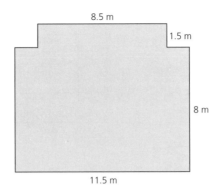

5. The room shown in Fig. 6.12 is to be laid with carpet squares 0.5 m by 0.5 m. How many carpet squares will be required to cover the floor? Also find the length of skirting board required to be placed around the room.

6. A flat roof is to be covered with a layer of adhesive and fibreglass. One container of adhesive will cover 12 m². If the roof is 8 m × 4 m, how many containers will have to be purchased?

7. A packet of weedkiller for a lawn will treat 5 m². If a lawn measures 12 m by 7 m, how many packets will be needed?

6.6 Volume

Volume is the space contained within a closed surface, such as the space inside a box or a balloon, shown in Fig. 6.13.

Fig. 6.13

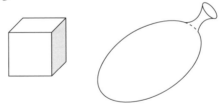

The unit of volume is a cube 1 m by 1 m by 1 m as shown in Fig. 6.14, called a cubic metre and written as 1 m³.

Fig. 6.14

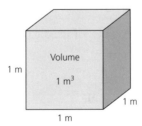

A cuboid 4 m long, 2 m wide and 3 m high is shown in Fig. 6.15. It can be divided into cubes 1 m × 1 m × 1 m to form 24 cubes.

Fig. 6.15

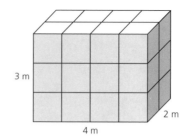

Volume = 24 m^3

that is   Volume = 4 × 2 × 3 = 24 m^3

It can be seen therefore that for any box of length L, width W and height H, shown in Fig. 6.16

Volume = Length × Width × Height

which can be shortened to the formula

V = L × W × H

Fig. 6.16

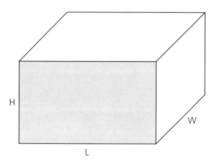

This formula can be used to find the volume of any box, when the lengths of the sides are known, as shown in Example 6.8.

EXAMPLE 6.8

Find the volume of a box of length 1.4 m, width 1.4 m and height 0.50 m.

Solution

Volume = L × W × H
= 1.4 × 1.4 × 0.50 m^3
= 0.98 m^3
= 1.0 m^3

Volume of a cube

A cube is a particular form of the cuboid described above, where all the sides are the same length, as shown in Fig. 6.17.

Fig. 6.17

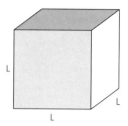

Volume of cube $= L \times L \times L = L^3$

EXAMPLE 6.9

Find the volume of a cube of sides of 4 cm.

Solution

Volume $= L^3 = 4 \times 4 \times 4 = 64$ cm^3

EXAMPLE 6.10

Coffee granules are packed into cartons 5 cm $\times$ 10 cm $\times$ 13 cm. How many cartons can be filled from a box 1.2 m $\times$ 0.7 m $\times$ 1.0 m which is full of coffee granules?

Solution

Note: Both volumes must be in the same units, preferably the smaller unit.

The dimensions of the box in centimetres are 120 cm $\times$ 70 cm $\times$ 100 cm

$$\text{Volume of box} = 120 \times 70 \times 100 \text{ cm}^3$$
$$= 840\ 000 \text{ cm}^3$$
$$\text{Volume of carton} = 5 \times 10 \times 13$$
$$= 650 \text{ cm}^3$$

The number of cartons is the number of 650 cm^3 in 840 000 cm^3

$$\text{Number of cartons} = 840\ 000 \div 650$$
$$= 1292.3$$
$$= 1292$$

The method of dividing volumes used in Example 6.10 cannot be used to decide how many solid objects can fit into a box, unless they fit inside exactly. A better method for this type of problem is shown in Example 6.11.

EXAMPLE 6.11

A video cassette measures 20 cm by 3 cm by 12 cm, as shown in Fig. 6.18 (a). How many can fit into a box 40 cm by 36 cm by 9 cm?

Solution

Fig. 6.18

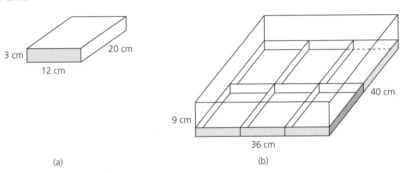

(a) (b)

First, we find how many lengths of the cassette will fit along the length of the box, that is, 40 ÷ 20 = 2.

Next we find how many widths of the cassette will fit along the width of the box, that is, 36 ÷ 12 = 3.

Therefore on the bottom of the box there will be a layer of 3 rows of 2, that is 6 cassettes, as shown in Fig. 6.18(b).

Finally we find how many layers can be placed in the box, that is 9 ÷ 3 = 3.

Therefore the number of cassettes is 3 layers of 6 = 18.

EXERCISE 6.2

1. Find the volumes of the following boxes:
    (i) 3 m × 2 m × 4 m   (ii) 3 cm × 6 cm × 5 cm   (iii) 2 ft × 4 ft × 2 ft

2. A carton of small tools measures 10 cm × 24 cm × 6 cm. They are packed by the manufacturer into boxes 96 cm × 40 cm × 72 cm. How many cartons will the box hold?

3. A cereal box measures 8 cm by 17 cm by 30 cm. If the cereal after packing settles to $\frac{7}{8}$ of the box, what is the volume of cereal in the box?

4. Fig. 6.19 is a tank which is full of food-flavouring liquid. Find the volume of the tank and hence how many 30 m*l* bottles can be filled from it.

Fig. 6.19

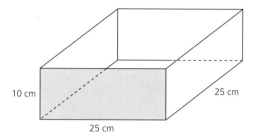

5. Fig. 6.20 shows a diagram of a room. The shaded square is a floor tile. Calculate
   (i) the area of the four walls
   (ii) the area of the floor
   (iii) the number of floor tiles required to tile the floor
   (iv) the volume of the room.

Fig. 6.20

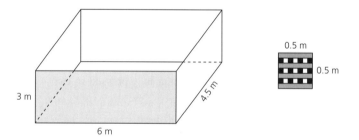

6. A trench is dug 1.5 m wide by 1.0 m deep by 40 m long. How many cubic metres of ready-mixed concrete are needed to fill the trench? If the ready-mix lorry delivers 7 m^3 at a time, how many loads are required? How much will be left over from the last load?

7. A tank for domestic central heating is 2 m long, 2 m wide and contains oil to the depth of 1 m. What is the volume of oil in litres in the tank? During winter months oil is used up at the rate of 200 l per week. How many weeks' supply is there in the tank?

8. A matchbox has dimensions 12 cm by 6 cm by 2 cm. How many matchboxes can be packed into a carton 36 cm by 24 cm by 24 cm?

9. For protection a delicate piece of glass is packed in a box 12 cm by 20 cm by 30 cm. This box is then placed inside another box 0.50 m by 0.50 m by 0.60 m. The space in between the two boxes is filled with polystyrene. What volume of poly-styrene is needed?

7 Plans and maps

7.1 Scales

Whenever something is to be built, such as a car, a house, a bridge, the details have to be worked out before starting. The starting point is a diagram on paper, which is a scaled-down version of the final object. Such diagrams are called plans or scale drawings. The plan becomes an exact replica but reduced in size. What is important is that lengths on the real object in any direction are always reduced by the same ratio on the plan.

A familiar example of this reduction is with maps, where distances on the ground are reduced by a large ratio on the map.

In other cases the plans are scaled up, but the same principle holds that a distance in any direction is always scaled up in the same ratio.

This change in size on the plan is expressed in two ways:

(i) a scale using dimensions such as 1 cm on the plan representing 1 m on the object;
(ii) a scale which is the ratio of the distance on the plan to the actual distance on the object. Thus, for example, using a ratio such as 1:1000 means that 1 cm on the plan represents 1000 cm on the object. The advantage of this scale ratio is that it can be used in any units of length – metres, kilometres, miles, feet, etc.

The scale as a ratio is found by writing both the actual length on the object and the length on the plan in the same units. Consider a scale of 1 cm to 1 m, then the scale as a ratio is

    1 cm to 100 cm = 1:100

This means that any length on the plan will be $\frac{1}{100}$ of an actual length on the object.

EXAMPLE 7.1

A road map is drawn to a scale of 2 cm to 10 km.
What is the scale as a ratio?

Solution

    Scale is 2 cm to 10 km.

Converting km to cm,

$$\text{scale is 2 cm to } 10 \times 1000 \text{ m}$$
$$= 2 \text{ cm to } 10 \times 1000 \times 100 \text{ cm}$$
$$= 2 \text{ cm to } 1\,000\,000 \text{ cm}$$

Scale as a ratio is 1:500 000

EXAMPLE 7.2

A plan of a garden is drawn to a scale which is in the ratio 1:300. What is this scale in centimetres to metres?

Solution

The scale as a ratio means that 1 cm on the plan represents 300 cm in the garden. Therefore

$$\text{scale is 1 cm to } 300 \text{ cm}$$
$$= 1 \text{ cm to } 3 \text{ m}$$

EXAMPLE 7.3

An atlas contains the map of Europe, and the scale is 4 cm to 500 km. Express this scale as a ratio.

Solution

$$\text{Scale is 4 cm to } 500 \text{ km}$$
$$= 4 \text{ cm to } 500 \times 1000 \text{ m}$$
$$= 4 \text{ cm to } 500 \times 1000 \times 100 \text{ cm}$$
$$= 4 \text{ cm to } 50\,000\,000 \text{ cm}$$

Scale as a ratio is 1:12 500 000

7.2 Converting distances using scales

To use scale drawings such as maps and plans it is necessary to carry out conversions between actual lengths and the scaled lengths on the drawing.

Consider the map shown in Fig. 7.1 which has a scale of 2 cm to 5 km. On the map is a line of electricity pylons going from A to B to C.

(a)   If AB on the map is 6 cm then the actual distance on the ground is calculated as follows:

2 cm on the map represents 5 km on the ground.
1 cm on the map represents 2.5 km on the ground.
AB = 6 cm on the map represents 2.5 × 6 km = 15 km on the ground.

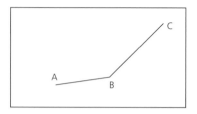

Fig. 7.1

(b) If the actual distance between B and C on the ground is 30 km then the length BC on the map is calculated as follows:

  5 km on the ground will be 2 cm on the map.

  1 km on the ground will be $\frac{2}{5}$ = 0.4 cm on the map.

BC representing 30 km on the ground will be 0.4 × 30 = 12 cm on the map.

A similar calculation is made when the scale is a ratio, as in Example 7.4.

EXAMPLE 7.4

A plan of a house is drawn to a scale 1:50. Find (i) the length of a wall which is 2 cm on the plan, (ii) the length on the plan of a wall of the house 12 m long.

Solution

  Scale is 1 cm to 50 cm.

 (i) A wall 2 cm on the plan will be 2 × 50 = 100 cm = 1 m in the house.
(ii) A length 50 cm in the house will be 1 cm on the plan

  1 cm in the house will be $\frac{1}{50}$ cm on the plan

  12 m = 1200 cm in the house will be $\frac{1}{50}$ × 1200 = 24 cm on the plan.

7.3 Suitable scales

In making a plan or drawing it is essential to decide on a convenient scale. Two examples of a scaling down are shown in Examples 7.5 and 7.6.

EXAMPLE 7.5

A rectangular garden, 10 m long and 4 m wide, is to be landscaped. In order to decide on the landscaping it is desirable to draw a plan to scale. Determine a suitable scale and then draw a plan to that scale.

Solution

The first requirement is to decide on a suitable scale of reduction. In so doing it is important to choose a scale that is easy to use, which means choosing simple numbers. It is also essential that the scale will allow the whole of the garden to be represented on the plan. A scale of 1 cm on the plan representing 1 m of the garden is suitable.

Therefore

the 10 m length of the garden will be 10 cm on the plan
the 4 m width of the garden will be 4 cm on the plan.

The plan of the garden is shown in Fig. 7.2.

Fig. 7.2

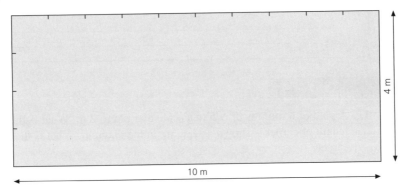

10 m

4 m

EXAMPLE 7.6

A rectangular table top is 1 m by 0.6 m. Using a suitable scale, make a scale drawing of the table top.

Solution

The table is 100 cm by 60 cm. A reasonable length on the drawing would be about 10 cm. Therefore a suitable scale would be 1 cm on the plan to represent 10 cm on the table.

Scale is

$$10 \text{ cm on the table will be} \quad 1 \text{ cm on the plan}$$
$$1 \text{ cm on the table will be} \quad \tfrac{1}{10} \text{ cm on the plan}$$
$$\text{the 100 cm length of the table will be } 100 \times \tfrac{1}{10} = 10 \text{ cm on the plan}$$
$$\text{the 60 cm width of the table will be } \quad 60 \times \tfrac{1}{10} = \quad 6 \text{ cm on the plan.}$$

The plan is shown in Fig. 7.3.

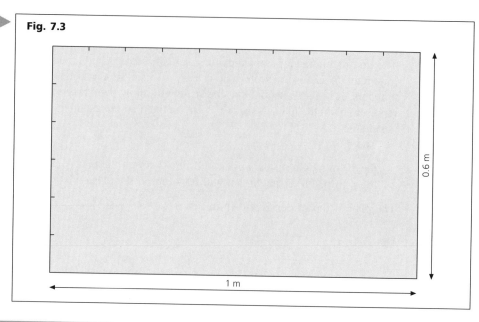

Fig. 7.3

0.6 m

1 m

1. A plan of a room is drawn to a scale of 1 cm to 2 m. What is the scale as a ratio? A length of carpet is shown as 2.5 cm on the diagram. What is the actual length of the carpet?

2. The plan of a sports ground is drawn to a scale of 2 cm to 5 m. Calculate the scale as a ratio. If the ground is 150 m by 120 m, what are these lengths on the plan? A cricket pitch, 22 m long, is drawn on the plan. What is the length of the pitch on the plan?

3. A plan of a garden is drawn to a scale of 1:100. If the garden is 30 m by 25 m, draw a plan to scale. If the lawn is 15 m square, calculate what this length would be on the plan.

4. A table top is 3 m by 2 m. In order to design a veneer pattern on it, a scale drawing is required. Decide on a suitable scale, and calculate what these dimensions would be on your drawing.

5. A dance hall is 50 m by 30 m. Using a scale of 1 cm to 2 m draw a scale diagram of the hall. If an emergency exit 2 m wide is at the centre of the 50 m length, show this to scale on the plan.

6. A patio, 5 m by 4 m, is to be laid in a garden. The patio slabs are $\frac{1}{2}$ m by $\frac{1}{2}$ m. Draw a plan of the patio to a suitable scale and show the patio squares on it.

7.4 Converting sketches to scale diagrams

The starting point of a project is often a series of sketches. These sketches are then converted into plans using a suitable scale.

EXAMPLE 7.7

Fig. 7.4 is a sketch of a plan of a room with a door and a window. Decide on a suitable scale and draw a plan to scale.

Fig. 7.4

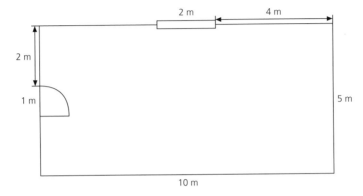

Solution

A suitable scale is 1 cm to 1 m, that is, every 1 m length on the sketch will be 1 cm long on the plan. The plan is shown in Fig. 7.5.

Fig. 7.5

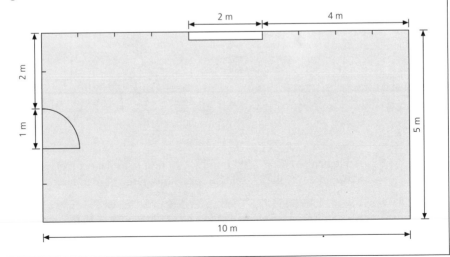

1. A garden has dimensions 20 m by 15 m. In the middle of the garden is a fishpond of diameter 10 m. Draw a plan of the garden to a suitable scale.

2. Fig. 7.6 shows the front of a garage. Draw a diagram to a suitable scale.

Fig. 7.6

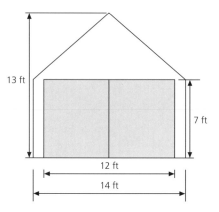

3. A floor of a room is 5 m by 4 m. A carpet is laid leaving a surround of 1 m. Draw to a suitable scale a plan of the floor area.

4. Fig. 7.7 shows a room in a café. It is carpeted with lengths of carpet 2 m wide, leaving a surround of 1 m wide all the way round. Using a suitable scale draw a plan of the café, showing the lengths of carpet.

Fig. 7.7

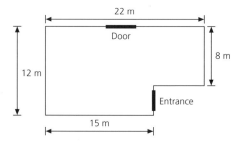

5. A kitchen worktop 1700 mm by 600 mm is to have a rectangular hole 860 mm by 420 mm cut from the middle for a sink. Draw a plan to scale of the worktop.

6. The sketch in Fig. 7.8 shows a bedroom 3.2 m by 2.7 m, with a door 0.8 m wide in the corner, and a window 1.2 m wide in the centre of the width. Draw a plan of the room to a suitable scale and include on the plan a possible layout of bedroom furniture of your choice.

Fig. 7.8

7. Fig. 7.9 shows a sketch of a garden with quarter circle flower beds at each corner of radius 5 m, and a central paved area 12 m × 5 m surrounded by a lawn. Draw the layout to a suitable scale.

Fig. 7.9

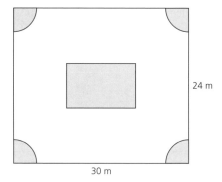

24 m

30 m

8. Fig. 7.10 shows a sketch of a running track, not drawn to scale, with semicircular ends. The width of the track is 12 m. Draw a plan of the track to scale and mark out the length for the 100 m race.

Fig. 7.10

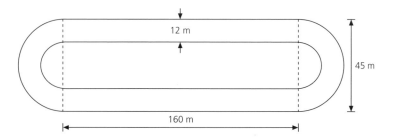

12 m

45 m

160 m

7.5 Maps

The scale on maps and atlases is often shown by a small ruler at the bottom of the map. An example is shown in Fig. 7.11 which is the scale on a road map. The length of ruler to the 5 km mark is 2 cm, which means that every 2 cm on the map represents 5 km on the ground.

Fig. 7.11

Scale is 2 cm to 5 km
            = 2 cm to 5 × 1000 × 100 cm
            = 2 cm to 500 000 cm
Scale as a ratio is 1:250 000

This means that the map is reduced 250 000 times.

A more detailed map showing minor roads and villages can be found in Ordnance Survey Landranger maps. These have a scale of 2 cm to 1 km, making the map larger than the road map. The scale, drawn on the map, is as shown in Fig. 7.12.

Fig. 7.12

Scale is 2 cm to 1 km
            = 2 cm to 1000 m
            = 2 cm to 1000 × 100 cm
            = 2 cm to 100 000 cm
Scale ratio is 1:50 000

In a map with this scale the distances on the ground are reduced 50 000 times.

EXAMPLE 7.8

The distance on a road map from Junction 11 to Junction 19 on the M5 motorway is 12 cm. What is the actual distance between the two junctions? The scale of the map is 1 cm to 5 km.

Solution

Scale is 1 cm to 5 km.

Therefore the distance 12 cm represents 12 × 5 = 60 km on the motorway.

EXAMPLE 7.9

The distance between Los Angeles and Houston, measured as a straight line on a map, is 11 cm. The scale of the map is 1:200 000 000. What is the actual distance between the two cities?

Solution

$$\text{Scale is } 1:20\ 000\ 000$$

Therefore   1 cm on the map is 20 000 000 cm on the ground

$$11 \text{ cm on the map is } 11 \times 20\ 000\ 000 \text{ cm}$$
$$= 11 \times 20\ 000\ 000 \div 100 \text{ m}$$
$$= 11 \times 200\ 000 \text{ m}$$
$$= 11 \times 200\ 000 \div 1000 \text{ km}$$
$$= 2200 \text{ km on the ground.}$$

EXERCISE 7.3

1. On a world atlas the British Isles are drawn to a scale of 4 cm to 47 km. What is the scale as a ratio? Two towns are 14 km apart. What is this distance on the map?

2. A road map is drawn to a scale of 2 cm to 5 km. The distance from Banbury to Warwick on the map is 11.8 cm. What is this distance in kilometres? Two towns are 35 km apart. What is the distance between them on the road map?

3. Fig. 7.13 shows a sketch of the Severn Bridge drawn to a scale of 2 m:5 km. Measure the distance between J22 and J23. Using the scale, calculate the actual distance on the motorway.

Fig. 7.13

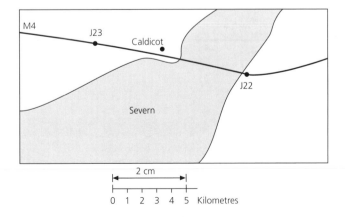

4. Fig. 7.14 shows a sketch of the coastline around The Wash, drawn to a scale shown on the ruler on the sketch. Measure the distance in centimetres across The Wash, from Boston to Hunstanton, and calculate the actual distance in kilometres.

Fig. 7.14

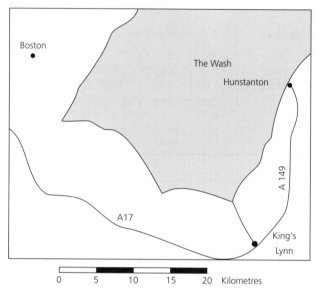

5. Fig. 7.15 shows a sketch map of the Isle of Wight, drawn to the scale shown as a ruler at the bottom of the map. Calculate the distances in km across the island from The Needles to Bembridge, and from Cowes to St Catherine's Point.

Fig. 7.15

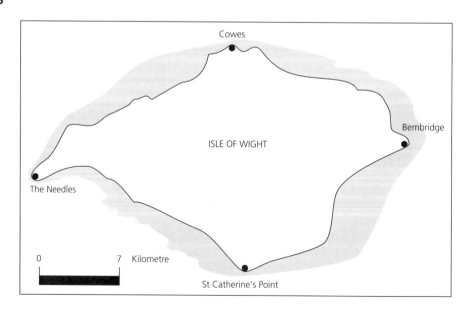

6. An atlas contains the map of Europe to the scale of 4 cm to 500 km. Express this scale as a ratio.

   What distance on the ground is represented by 3 cm on the map?

   What length on the map represents 1250 km on the ground?

7. An Ordnance Survey Explorer map has a scale of 4 cm to 1 km. Express this scale as a ratio. Such a map shows two churches which are 3.6 cm apart on the map. How far apart are they on the ground?

8. A Michelin route-planning map is drawn to a scale of 1:1 000 000. The length of the road on the map between two towns is 7.8 cm. What is the actual distance in kilometres between these two towns?

9. A party of students checked the length of a proposed hike on an OS Landranger map which has a scale ratio of 1:50 000. If the length of the hike on the map was 34.5 cm, what distance will they actually walk?

8 Formulae and graphs I

8.1 Formulae

In chapter 6 an introduction was given to the use of formulae. The area of a rectangle was written as

$$A = L \times W$$

where L is the length of the rectangle and W its width. Also, the volume V of a box was given as

$$V = L \times W \times H$$

where L is the length of the box, W its width and H its height. Numbers can be *substituted* for L, W and H to find the volume of a particular size of box. The importance of formulae is that once they have been established the calculations become routine. A calculation using a formula is shown in Example 8.1.

EXAMPLE 8.1

Find the area A of a rectangle with a length of 12 cm and a width of 18 cm.

Solution

The formula for the area is $A = L \times W$
For this particular rectangle

$$L = 12 \text{ cm}, \ W = 18 \text{ cm}$$

These values are substituted into the formula

$$A = 12 \times 18$$
$$= 216 \text{ cm}^2$$

8.2 Examples of formulae

Formula for the simple interest on money deposited in a bank

When a sum of money is deposited in a bank or building society it is used to finance other business, and for this a payment is made to the depositor. This payment is called interest. When the money is left in for a year the total interest earned is the *annual interest*.

There are two types of interest:

(i) simple interest, where the annual interest is withdrawn by the depositor;
(ii) compound interest, where the annual interest is added to the sum deposited, so that the interest the following year will be on a larger sum.

In order to establish the formula for the simple interest a calculation is first made with actual numbers.

Let £200 be deposited in a building society with simple interest at an annual rate of 5% for 3 years.

In the 1st year the interest is 5% of £200 $= \frac{5}{100} \times £200 = £10$

In the 2nd year the interest is the same $\quad = £10$
In the 3rd year the interest is the same $\quad = £10$
Total interest for 3 years $\qquad\qquad = £30$ that is,

Total interest = Annual interest × Number of years.

Let £P be deposited in a building society with simple interest at an annual rate of R% for T years.

Using the same process to get the formula,

For one year the interest is R% of £P $= \dfrac{R}{100} \times P$

For T years the interest $= \dfrac{R}{100} \times P \times T.$

The formula for simple interest is

$$I = \frac{P \times R \times T}{100}$$

The '×' is often omitted and understood to be in the formula, so that it becomes

$$I = \frac{PRT}{100}$$

The use of this formula in calculating simple interest is shown in Example 8.2.

EXAMPLE 8.2

Find the simple interest obtained by investing £300 at an annual rate of 7% over 4 years.

Solution

Using the formula for simple interest

$$I = \frac{PRT}{100}$$

with P = £300
R = 7%
T = 4 years

Substitute these values for the letters in the formula:

$$I = \frac{300 \times 7 \times 4}{100}$$
$$= £84$$

Speed, time and distance

The speed of a car or any moving body states how far it moves in a given unit of time, that is 1 s or 1 hour.

For example, if a car travels 40 m in 1 second its speed is 40 m/s. Therefore, a car moving at 40 m/s travels

40 m in 1 second
80 m in 2 seconds
120 m in 3 seconds

In this example the distance travelled is found by multiplying the speed in m/s by the time in seconds. Writing this as a formula with

speed as s
time as t
distance as d

the distance travelled in this time is

d = s × t

EXAMPLE 8.3

The speed of a car is 40 miles per hour. How far will it travel in 6 hours without stopping?

Solution

Using the formula

$$d = s \times t$$

where $s = 40$ miles/hour
$\quad\quad\quad t = 6$ hours
distance $d = 40 \times 6$
$\quad\quad\quad\quad = 240$ miles

Cost of hiring a car

To hire a car for a week the car hire firm makes

a basic charge of £150 for a week
a mileage charge of 14p per mile travelled.

If the car travels 250 miles in a week

the mileage charge $= 14 \times 250$ pence
$$= £\tfrac{14}{100} \times 250$$
$$= £35$$

Therefore, total charge $= £150 + £35$
$$= £185$$

Writing this as a formula where

B is the basic charge in pounds (£)
C is the mileage charge in pence per mile
N is the number of miles travelled
H is the total hiring charge in pounds (£)

then

$$H = B + \frac{C}{100} \times N$$

or

$$H = B + \frac{CN}{100}$$

EXAMPLE 8.4

A plant hire firm makes a basic charge of £30 to hire a power strimmer for a week, and 90p per day for any period after a week.
If a customer hired the strimmer for 8 days in addition to the basic week, how much did he pay?

Solution

Basic charge B = £30
Cost per day C = 90p
Number of days N = 8

$$\text{Hire charge } H = B + \frac{C}{100} \times N$$

$$= 30 + \frac{90}{100} \times 8$$

$$= 30 + 0.9 \times 8$$

$$= 30 + 7.20$$

$$= £37.20$$

Cost of electricity

All electrical appliances use electrical power at different rates which are given as power ratings in *watts*. Electricity is charged according to the number of units of electricity used. The unit is based on the kilowatt (kW). The unit of electricity is the amount of electricity used when an appliance with a power rating of 1 kilowatt, that is 1000 watts, is switched on for 1 hour.

Therefore if an appliance, rated at 500 watts, is switched on for 3 hours the number of units of electricity is found as follows:

Power rating in kilowatts $= \frac{50}{1000} = \frac{1}{2}$

Time switched on = 3 h

Units used $= 3 \times \frac{1}{2} = 1.5$

The formula for the cost of electricity is obtained as follows.
If the power rating of the appliance is W watts and the number of hours is H then

Power rating in kilowatts is $= \frac{W}{1000}$

Number of units $= \frac{W}{1000} \times H$

If a unit costs P pence then the total cost C in pence is

$$C = \frac{W}{1000} \times H \times P$$

$$C = \frac{WHP}{1000}$$

EXAMPLE 8.5

A small electric heater has a power rating of 250 watts. If a unit of electricity costs 7p, find the cost of running the heater for 2 hours.

Solution

Using the formula $\quad C = \dfrac{WHP}{1000}$

where $\quad W = 250$ watts, $H = 2$ hours, $P = 7p$

$$C = \frac{250 \times 2 \times 7}{1000} = 3\tfrac{1}{2}p$$

The circumference and area of a circle

Fig. 8.1 shows the parts of a circle.

Fig. 8.1

The edge of the circle is always at a fixed distance from a point O.
    The point O is the *centre of the circle*.
    This fixed distance from the point O to the edge is the *radius* r.
    The line from one point on the edge, through the centre, to the edge on the other side is the *diameter* d.

 (i)   From Fig. 8.1 it is seen that
        $d = 2r$
 (ii) The distance around the edge of the circle is called the *circumference* C. The circumference C is given by the formula
        $C = \pi d$
        where π is a constant $= 3.142$
 (iii) The area A enclosed by the circumference is given by
        $A = \pi r^2$
        where r^2 is in the form of indices and means $r \times r$

EXAMPLE 8.6

Using the above formulae find the diameter, circumference and area of a circle of radius 3 cm.

Solution

(i) Diameter $\quad$ d = 2r $\quad$ where r = 3 cm
$$d = 2 \times 3$$
$$= 6 \text{ cm}$$

(ii) Circumference C = πd $\quad$ where d = 6 cm
$$C = 3.14 \times 6$$
$$= 18.8 \text{ cm}$$

(iii) Area $\quad$ A = πr^2 $\quad$ where r = 3 cm
$$A = 3.14 \times 3 \times 3$$
$$= 3.14 \times 9$$
$$= 28.3 \text{ cm}^2$$

EXERCISE 8.1

1. Find the volume of a box with the measurements
length = 4 cm $\quad$ width = 3 cm $\quad$ height = 3.5 cm.

2. Find the area of a rectangle which has a length of 0.7 m and a width of 0.46 m.

3. A cyclist travels at an average speed of 8 m/s. How far will he travel in 20 min?

4. A platoon of soldiers marched at 4 miles per hour for $2\frac{1}{2}$ hours. What was the total distance marched?

5. If an electric iron, rated at 300 watts, is used for 2 hours, find how much this costs if the unit cost of electricity is 7.2p.

6. Calculate the circumference and area of a circle if its radius is 5 cm.

7. A car travels at a steady speed of 60 km/h for 1.2 hours. What is the distance covered in this time?

8. A circular mirror has a diameter of 22 cm. Find the area of the glass in the mirror and the length of the circular frame around the mirror.

9. Find the simple interest on £500 for 6 years if the annual rate is 5%.

10. What area of plastic sheet is required to cover a fishpond 2.4 m in diameter to protect it from freezing?

8.3 Graphs

A graph is a pictorial method of showing how one quantity depends upon another. It consists of a set of points through which a line can be drawn to show how the two quantities are related. The steps in drawing graphs are shown below.

Locating a point on a page

The shaded rectangle in Fig. 8.2 is a diagram of a page. In order to fix any point P at a particular position on the page, two reference lines OX and OY are drawn. These two reference lines are called *axes*, OX being the x-axis and OY the y-axis.

To fix the position of a point P two lengths are required which can be drawn from two reference lines OX and OY. One length is the distance PA from the axis OX, the other length is the distance PC from the axis OY.

Fig. 8.2

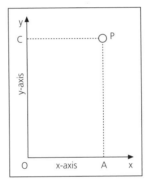

EXAMPLE 8.7

Draw the x and y axes on a sheet of paper. Plot the point P on it which is 6 cm from the x-axis and 5 cm from the y-axis.

Solution

In Fig. 8.3 the two axes are drawn perpendicular to one another.
A vertical line AB is drawn 5 cm from the y-axis.
A horizontal line CD is drawn 6 cm from the x-axis.
The point of intersection P is the required point, which is 5 cm from the y-axis and 6 cm from the x-axis.
The two distances are placed in brackets after the point, showing that P is 5 cm along the x-axis and 6 cm along the y-axis. These two values are called *co-ordinates*. The first number is always the x-distance, the second number the y-distance.

Fig. 8.3

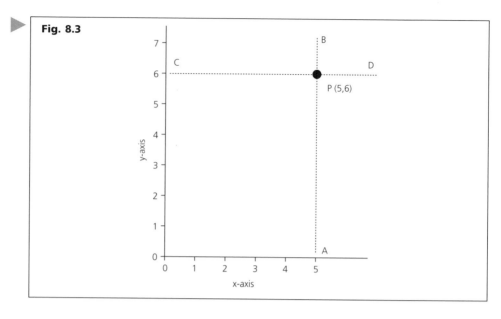

Graph paper

A sheet of graph paper is covered with a grid of lines as shown in Fig. 8.4. The whole page is divided into large squares and the large squares further divided into tenths. These vertical and horizontal grid lines can then be used with a suitable scale marked on them to locate a point such as P in Fig. 8.3. This avoids the need for measurement each time a point is to be marked on the paper.

Axes

In order to create these measuring scales a pair of axes is drawn along a suitable horizontal and vertical grid line. Where the axes cross is the reference point, called the *origin*.

Fig. 8.4

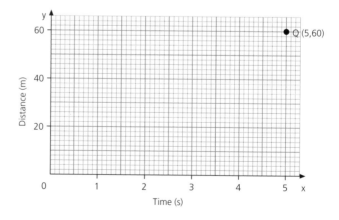

Scales

The axes can be used to mark units of measurement on a graph, such as time, area, length, temperature, etc. To accommodate different sizes of these units suitable scales are marked on the axes. The scale on the y-axis need not be the same as the scale on the x-axis. In Fig. 8.4, in order to be able to plot the point Q which represents a distance 60 m travelled in 5 s, the x-axis is marked in seconds with each large division being 1 s. The y-axis is marked in metres with each large division being 20 m. The co-ordinates (5,60) mean that Q is 5 s along the x-axis and 60 m along the y-axis.

Certain scales on the large divisions are difficult to use, for example 3, 7, 9 etc. Such scales would sub-divide into the small divisions as 0.3, 0.7, 0.9 which are awkward to use, and therefore to be avoided. Suitable scales for the large divisions are 1, 2, 5, 10, 20, etc.

The process of fixing a point is now extended to include a series of points, which involves deciding and choosing a suitable scale. The process is done step by step in Example 8.8.

EXAMPLE 8.8

A cyclist travels along a road and covers the following number of miles:

> In 1 hour : 12 miles
> In 3 hours : 36 miles
> In 5 hours : 60 miles
> In 6 hours : 72 miles

Show these values on graph paper.

Solution

(i) The first step is to decide on the axes. When one of the units is time it is customary to place it on the x-axis.
(ii) The second step is to determine the scale for each axis.

It is important to choose the scale that is easy to use. Each large division is chosen to represent a round figure.

The largest number of hours is 6. On the graph shown in Fig. 8.5 there are 6 large divisions on the horizontal axis. To get 6 hours on the paper a scale of 1 hour per large division can be used.

The number of miles is placed on the y-axis. In Fig. 8.5 there are 4 large divisions on the vertical axis. The maximum number of miles is 72. To decide on a scale divide the maximum miles by the number of squares, that is, $72 \div 4 = 18$. This is then rounded to a convenient figure of 20 miles per large division, making each small division equal to 2 miles. This scale makes it easy to plot points.

The set of values are shown in Fig. 8.5.

Fig. 8.5

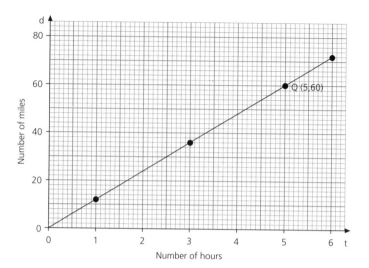

The set of points are seen to lie on a straight line. This happens when values of points obey a simple formula. In this case the formula is

Distance = Speed × Time
$$d = s \times t$$

EXAMPLE 8.9

A store lists the price of various lengths of material as follows.

    4 m   £6
    6 m   £9
    8 m   £12
  10 m   £13
  12 m   £18

Plot a graph of these values and find the item which appears to be wrongly priced. From the graph find the price of a length of 2.4 m.

Solution

The length of material is placed along the x-axis.
    In Fig. 8.6

      number of large divisions from the origin = 6
            maximum length of material = 12 m
               scale per large division = 12 ÷ 6 = 2

This is a convenient number for a scale.

Fig. 8.6

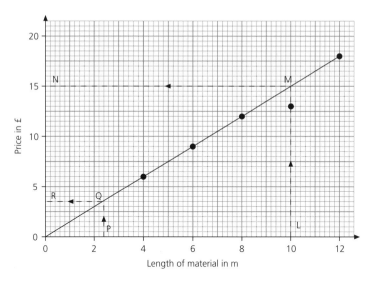

Length of material in m

The price is placed along the y-axis:

number of large divisions from the origin = 5
maximum price = £18
scale per large division = 18 ÷ 5 = 3.6

For convenience this is rounded to 5 per large division.

Using these scales a graph is plotted in Fig. 8.6.

From the graph it is seen that all the points lie on a straight line, except the price of the 10 m length. This suggests that the price of this length is incorrect. By drawing the line LMN it is seen that the price is likely to be £15.

From the line PQR the length of 2.4 m is priced at £3.50.

8.4 Plotting a graph of a formula

If we start with a formula we can obtain co-ordinates from it.

Consider that in a supermarket the price of a small packet of biscuits is 80p. Therefore

2 packets will cost 80 × 2
3 packets will cost 80 × 3
N packets will cost 80 × N

Therefore the formula for cost C is

$$C = 80N$$

Using the formula the cost is found of 2, 4, 6, 8, 10 packets

Number N	Cost C (pence)
2	160
4	320
6	480
8	640
10	800

A quantity on the left of a formula, in this case C, is usually placed on the y-axis. The number of packets N is, therefore, placed on the x-axis.
   In Fig. 8.7

   number of large divisions from the origin = 6
         maximum number of packets N = 10
            scale per large division = 10 ÷ 6 = 1.7

For convenience this is rounded to 2 packets per large division.

   Number of large divisions from the origin = 4
               Maximum cost C = 800 pence
         Scale per large division = 800 ÷ 4 = 200

200p per large division is a convenient scale.
   The graph of costs is shown in Fig. 8.7.

Fig. 8.7

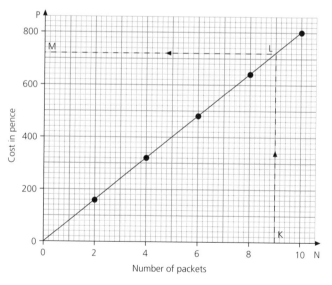

The cost of any other number of packets can then be read off the graph. Thus, the cost of 9 packets is found by drawing KLM from the x-axis to the y-axis.

   Cost of 9 packets = value at M = 720p

1. Which of the following numbers will make a convenient scale per large division on an axis? For the ones that you choose, what is the scale per small division of the axis?

   0.3, 0.5, 1, 2, 5, 6, 7, 9, 10, 12, 15, 20, 30, 70, 100

2. For each of the following ranges, decide on a suitable scale:
   (i) Number of large divisions 6, highest value to be plotted 30
   (ii) Number of large divisions 7, highest value to be plotted 32
   (iii) Number of large divisions 4, highest value to be plotted 60
   (iv) Number of large divisions 8, highest value to be plotted 72

3. The graph in Fig. 8.8 shows the costs a storekeeper has calculated for numbers of power tools. Which number is costed incorrectly? By drawing a straight line, what should the correct cost be?

Fig. 8.8

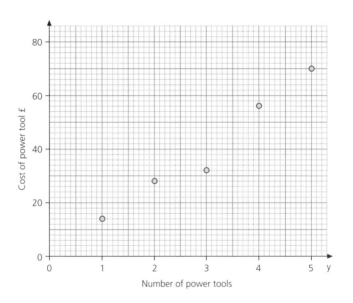

4. The table shows temperatures on the Celsius and Fahrenheit scales.

Temperature °C	0	20	30	40	50	60
Temperature °F	32	68	86	104	122	140

Choose a suitable scale and plot a graph of these temperatures. From the graph find (i) what 35 °F is in Celsius, (ii) what 42 °C is in Fahrenheit.

5. The area of a rectangle of width 10 cm and length L is given by A = 10 L. Complete a table of the areas of rectangles for values of L of 2, 4, 6, 8, 10 cm. Draw a graph of these values. From the graph find the area of the rectangle where L = 5.3 cm.

6. A car is travelling at a speed of 40 km/h. The formula for distance travelled is
   $d = st$
   From the formula find the distances covered by the car in a range of time from 0 to
   6 hours, and plot a graph of the numbers. From the graph find
   (i) how far the car will travel in 2.25 hours
   (ii) how long the car will take to travel 170 km.

7. The simple interest I earned in one year on a deposit of £2000 is given by
   $I = 20R$
   where R is the annual rate %.
   Plot a graph to show how the interest earned in that year varied as the rate of
   interest varies from 3% to 9%. From the graph find the interest earned when the rate
   is 5.5% and the rate that will give an annual interest of £165.

8. The cost of hiring a video recorder is given by
   $C = 10 + 2W$
   where C is the cost in £ and W is the number of weeks. Draw a graph showing the
   cost of hire for a range of weeks from 1 to 25. From your graph find (i) the initial
   deposit that you must pay, (ii) the weekly rental charge.

9 Data handling I

9.1 Data collecting

When a large amount of information is gathered in the form of numbers it is necessary to have methods of organising this information into a form that makes it understandable and useful. These methods make up the subject called *statistics*.

Numerical data comes from many sources such as

(i)   written sources of statistical data issued by the government;

(ii) results from experiments and measurements;

(iii) surveys using questionnaires, such as market research and the National Census every 10 years of all the people living in the UK.

The quantity of information collected in this way is so large that the numbers can make no sense in themselves. The information is grouped according to certain principles to bring out any pattern or trends.

9.2 Presenting and interpreting data

Consider an everyday situation of a shoe shop selling trainers. In a typical day 20 pairs of trainers were sold in various sizes. The sizes were recorded as the trainers were sold:

```
6  5  4  6  6
6  3  5  5  4
5  5  7  6  6
7  4  6  5  6
```

In this form these numbers provide little information. They now need to be grouped into a table listing how many were sold in each size. The number sold in each size is called the *frequency*. This has been done in Table 9.1, called a *frequency table*. A tally is kept of the numbers sold in each size and entered in the table.

It is important to add up the frequency column as a check that all the original records have been included.

Table 9.1

Size of trainer	Number of pairs	
	Tally	Frequency
3	I	1
4	III	3
5	ℕℕ I	6
6	ℕℕ III	8
7	II	2
	Total	20

With the data arranged in 5 groups, called *classes*, it is now easier to see the sales pattern:

- The most popular size is size 6.
- The trainers sold are clustered around sizes 5 and 6.
- The trainers vary in size from size 3 to size 7.

9.3 Range and class interval

Consider another situation where a number of people in a slimming class were weighed and the data recorded to the nearest kilogram as follows:

```
44   45   51   48
47   59   48   40
43   58   49   54
45   47   52   51
```

We need to examine this data first of all because it is different from the data collected about the sales of trainers. Since all the weights are rounded to the nearest kilogram, a recorded weight of 40 kg could actually be any weight from 39.5 kg up to 40.5 kg; a recorded weight of 41 kg could be from 40.5 up to 41.5, and so on for all the weights up to 59 kg, which could be from 58.5 kg up to 59.5 kg.

(i) Range
     The range of the data is defined as the (largest value – smallest value).
     For this data range = 59 – 40 = 19 kg.
     We see that the range is a measure of how spread out are the values in the set.

(ii) Number of classes
      To obtain the class interval the first step is to decide on the number of classes. Between 4 and 10 classes are normally used, depending upon the range and the quantity of data. In this example, with only 16 weights 4 classes are appropriate.

(iii) Class interval
       The class interval is the spread of values in each class, which is found from

       class interval = range ÷ number of classes

       In this example class interval = 20 ÷ 4 = 5 kg to the nearest kilogram.

Therefore the class intervals are 39.5 up to 44.5 kg, 44.5 up to 49.5 kg, etc. as shown in Table 9.2. A tally of the data is also in shown in Table 9.2.

Table 9.2

Weight in kg (nearest kg)	Weight in kg (class interval)	Tally (no. of people)	Frequency
40–44	39.5 up to 44.5	III	3
45–49	44.5 up to 49.5	THH II	7
50–54	49.5 up to 54.5	IIII	4
55–59	54.5 up to 59.5	II	2
		Total	16

9.4 Discrete and continuous data

The data in sections 9.2 and 9.3 are different types of data which need examining.

(i) Discrete data
     In the case of the trainers, the sizes go up in steps, and the numbers sold refer to specific sizes. This type of data is called *discrete data*. Another example is counting the number of screws in boxes.

(ii) Continuous data
      In section 9.3 where the weights were being measured, although the weights were recorded to the nearest kilogram, the actual weights were likely to be anywhere in the range. Such data is called *continuous data*. Another example is the time taken by different people to complete a task.

In general, counting produces discrete data and measuring produces continuous data.

9.5 Pictorial representation

Grouped data can be represented pictorially with

    frequency polygons
    bar charts
    histograms
    pie charts

These charts help to show patterns and trends within the data. They aid the process of reaching conclusions about the data.

Frequency polygons

If we return to section 9.2 and the example with trainers, the frequency is plotted against size, as shown in Fig. 9.1. The graph in Fig. 9.1 is called a frequency polygon.

Fig. 9.1

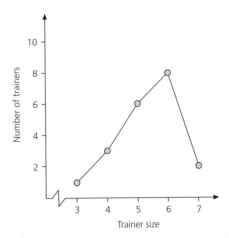

The data in section 9.3 is also plotted as a frequency polygon in Fig. 9.2. The number of people is plotted against the mid point of each class, which is 42 kg, 47 kg, 52 kg, 57 kg.

Fig. 9.2

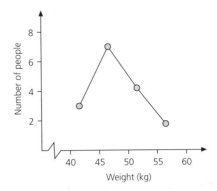

Bar charts

Bar charts are used with discrete data, where the frequencies are represented by heights of bars drawn at the class value. Fig. 9.3 shows a bar chart drawn from Table 9.1 for the sale of trainers.

Once the data has been displayed as a bar chart it is then easier to interpret it.

Fig. 9.3

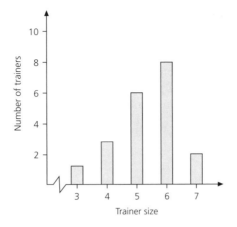

Trainer size

EXAMPLE 9.1

A factory packs screws into boxes and a sample of boxes is checked to count the number of screws in each box. The results are shown in Fig. 9.4.

From the diagram

(i) what was the size of the sample?

(ii) what percentage of boxes were below the standard of 50 screws per box?

Fig. 9.4

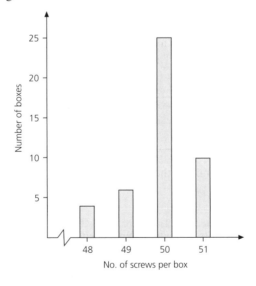

No. of screws per box

Solution

(i) Size of sample = total height of the bars
$$= 4 + 6 + 25 + 10 = 45 \text{ boxes}$$

(ii) Boxes below standard are the height of the bars for the classes less than 50.

Number $= 4 + 6 = 10$

Percentage $= \frac{10}{45} \times 100 = 22.2$

Histograms

In the case of the weights of people in the slimming class in section 9.3 the data is continuous over the whole range and the class intervals run into one another. The widths of the bars are now equal to the class intervals. The resulting chart is called a histogram. Histograms are more appropriate for displaying continuous data such as this. Fig. 9.5 displays the histogram of the data in Table 9.2.

Fig. 9.5

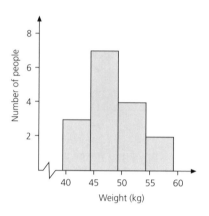

Weight (kg)

EXAMPLE 9.2

Thirty office workers took part in a trial to see how long they took to complete a form-filling exercise. The times taken were recorded to the nearest minute as shown in the following table:

Time in minutes	20	21	22	23	24	25
Number of workers	2	6	8	10	3	1

Draw a histogram of the results.

Solution

Since the results in the table have been rounded off to the nearest minute, the actual times taken can be anywhere in the range. The class intervals are:

19.5 up to 20.5 min
20.5 up to 21.5 min
21.5 up to 22.5 min
22.5 up to 23.5 min
23.5 up to 24.5 min
24.5 up to 25.5 min

The histogram is shown in Fig. 9.6.

Fig. 9.6

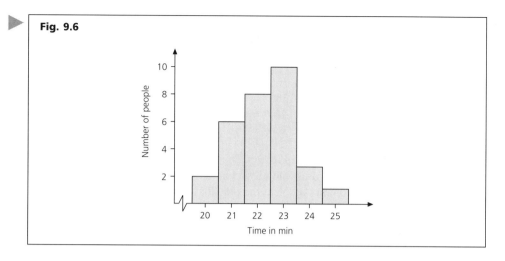

Pie charts

A pie chart forms a picture of the data in the form of sectors of a circle as shown in Fig. 9.7. Each sector represents a class. The size of the angle at the centre of each sector is proportional to the number of items in each class.

Fig. 9.7

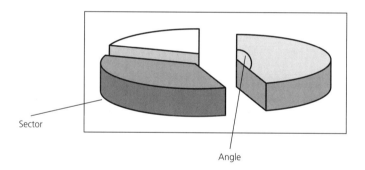

To show how a pie chart is constructed, consider the following table which is the result of a survey of heating systems in a district:

Heating system	% of houses
Oil	40
Gas	36.7
Coal	13.3
Electricity	10

The angle at the centre of a circle is 360°.

Each of these heating systems will be represented by a sector, whose angle will be proportional to the % of houses in each group, that is,

$$\text{oil} : 40\% \quad \text{of } 360° = 144°$$
$$\text{gas} : 36.7\% \text{ of } 360° = 132°$$
$$\text{coal} : 13.3\% \text{ of } 360° = 48°$$
$$\text{electricity} : 10\% \quad \text{of } 360° = 36°$$

The pie chart is shown in Fig. 9.8. Draw a circle and a radius. From this radius measure an angle of 144° to draw the oil sector. Then measure an angle of 132° to draw the gas sector, and so on, to complete the pie chart.

Fig. 9.8

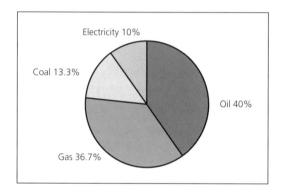

EXAMPLE 9.3

An industrial company employed the following types of technicians:

Type	Number
Mechanical	12
Electrical	8
Building	5
Plant	15

Show these figures on a pie chart.

Solution

The angles of sectors on the pie chart will be proportional to the number of technicians.

Total number of technicians = 40

Fraction of mechanical technicians = $\frac{12}{40}$; angle of sector = $\frac{12}{40} \times 360° = 108°$

Fraction of electrical technicians = $\frac{8}{40}$; angle of sector = $\frac{8}{40} \times 360° = 72°$

Fraction of building technicians = $\frac{5}{40}$; angle of sector = $\frac{5}{40} \times 360° = 45°$

Fraction of plant technicians = $\frac{15}{40}$; angle of sector = $\frac{15}{40} \times 360° = 135°$

The pie chart is shown in Fig. 9.9.

Fig. 9.9

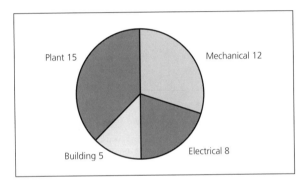

1. The number of goals scored per match by a team over 20 matches was as follows:

0	1	2	1	3
0	1	0	1	3
1	0	1	1	0
1	2	2	2	3

   Show these results pictorially using a bar chart.

2. The waist measurements, to the nearest cm, of 25 fashion students were

57	62	64	59	64
67	64	60	58	60
63	66	63	65	62
63	67	65	65	67
70	70	67	65	65

   Group these data into 5 classes, 56–58, 59–61, etc., find the class intervals, and draw a histogram. Comment on the shape of the chart.

3. The two tables below give the part-time earnings of male and female students.

Earnings	£1–£6	£7–£12	£13–£18	£19–£24	£25–£30
No. of males	3	11	11	16	4
No. of females	5	15	9	6	8

Draw the frequency polygon for both groups of students on the same axes and compare the earning patterns of both groups.

4. The ages of people staying in a residential home were:

Ages	Number of people
65–69	4
70–74	8
75–79	12
80–84	9
Over 85	3

Draw a pie chart of the table.

5. A survey of faults on televisions was recorded as follows:
   Transistors   30
   Assembly   86
   Capacitor   32
   Tube   14
   Resistor   18
   Draw a pie chart of the results.

6. A check was made on the weights of coffee in 200 g jars, with the following results:

Weight (g)	198	199	200	201	202	203
No. of packets	1	3	4	6	12	4

Represent these data pictorially by drawing a histogram.

7. A machine packs paper clips into boxes of 100. A check was made on a sample of 25 boxes, and they were found to contain the following numbers of clips:

Number of clips per box	92	96	100	104	108
No. of boxes	5	8	15	21	3

Show these results on a bar chart.

8. The bar chart in Fig. 9.10 shows the number of children per family in a certain group.

Fig. 9.10

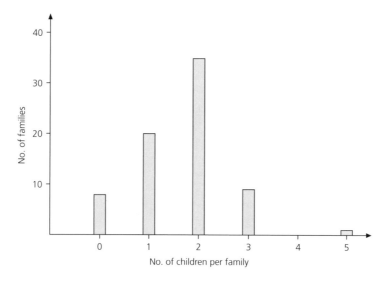

From Fig. 9.10

(i) How many families are there in the group?
(ii) What is the range of the data?
(iii) What is the most popular number of children per family?
(iv) What percentage of these families have
no children?
2 or more children?
4 children?

9.6 Average and range

The concept of average in statistics is used in three ways, namely *mean*, *median* and *mode*.

Mean value of a set of numbers

Consider the midday temperatures recorded over a 7-day period.

23 °C, 24 °C, 25 °C, 26 °C, 20 °C, 23 °C, 27 °C.

These temperatures are shown on a bar chart in Fig. 9.11. If the various heights of the bars are evened out they would all be at a height of 24 °C.
24 °C is said to be the average or mean temperature of these 7 values.

Fig. 9.11

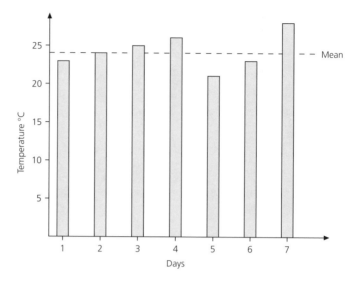

The mean can be calculated by adding the 7 temperatures and dividing by 7, that is

$$\text{mean temperature} = \frac{23 + 24 + 25 + 26 + 20 + 23 + 27}{7}$$

$$= \frac{168}{7}$$

$$= 24 \,°\text{C}$$

The formula for the mean is

$$\text{Mean} = \frac{\text{Sum of all values}}{\text{Number of values}}$$

EXAMPLE 9.4

The times taken, in minutes, for 9 people to complete a task were
10, 13, 12, 14, 16, 11, 12, 15, 12

Find the mean value of these times taken.

Solution

The sum of all the times taken $= 10 + 13 + 12 + 14 + 16 + 11 + 12 + 15 + 12$
$$= 115$$
The number of tasks $= 9$

Mean time to complete the tasks $= \frac{115}{9} = 12.8$ min

Mode

The mode of a set of numbers is the value that occurs most often.

In Example 9.4 the set of times are arranged in increasing order,

10, 11, 12, 12, 12, 13, 14, 15, 16

The time of 12 min occurs most often. Hence

mode = 12 min

Median

The median of a set of numbers is the value of the middle number when the set is arranged in increasing order.

Referring to Example 9.4 again and arranging the times in increasing order:

$$\downarrow$$
10, 11, 12, 12, 12, 13, 14, 15, 16

The middle value is the 5th along the line, with 4 numbers on either side. Hence

median = 12 min

The median can easily be identified when the series of numbers is odd, as in the above case. When the set of numbers is even the middle pair of numbers is identified, and the mean of these two numbers is taken as the median, as shown in Example 9.5.

EXAMPLE 9.5

Over a 10-day period the temperature at midday was recorded in °C as
19, 22, 25, 22, 26, 23, 22, 25, 26, 20

Find the mean, mode and median temperatures.

Solution

(i) Mean temperature
  Sum of all readings = 19 + 22 + 25 + 22 + 26 + 23 + 22 + 25 + 26 + 20
  $\qquad\qquad\qquad\qquad$ = 230 °C
  Number of readings = 10
  Mean temperature $\quad = \frac{230}{10} = 23$ °C

(ii) Mode and median

The readings are arranged in increasing order:

$$\downarrow \quad \downarrow$$

19 20 22 22 22 23 25 25 26 26

The temperature occurring most often is 22 °C.

mode = 22 °C

The median is found from the middle pair because the number of readings is even, that is

median = $\frac{22 + 23}{2}$ = 22.5 °C

The average of a set of numbers is the value about which the set appears to be clustered or grouped. Each average has its advantages/disadvantages, depending on the particular application.

The mean is used extensively because all numbers in the set are used to calculate it, but it can be badly affected by a single very large or very small number among the set.

The median has the advantage that it is the middle number irrespective of any unusually large or small numbers in the set, but it does not take into account the values of the numbers in the set.

The mode is useful to find what value is occurring most often, such as the title of the compact disc with the greatest sales, but it can be misleading as an average if it occurs near the end of the range.

9.7 Comparison using mean and range

The mean and the range are useful for comparing two sets of data, as shown by the following example.

Three students sat the same examinations and the mean of the marks obtained by each student is shown in the table. In addition, the range of the marks for each student is also shown.

	Mean mark	Range mark
Mary	50	5
Tom	50	20
Richard	75	10

Tom and Mary have the same mean mark, but Tom's large range shows that he has low marks in some examinations and high marks in others.

Mary has been consistent with all her examination marks near 50.

Richard has a good mean mark, and the reasonably small range suggests that all his marks are fairly close to 75.

EXAMPLE 9.6

In 6 innings in test matches a batsman makes scores of

40, 56, 100, 83, 34, 71

Calculate his mean score and range.

Solution

Total runs scored = 40 + 56 + 100 + 83 + 34 + 71
= 384
Number of innings = 6
Mean score = $\frac{384}{6}$ = 64
Range = highest score − lowest score
= 100 − 34
= 68

EXAMPLE 9.7

Another batsman over the same 6 innings has a mean score of 60 runs and a range of 15 runs. Compare this batsman with the one in Example 9.6. How many runs did this batsman make altogether?

Solution

This batsman has a slightly lower mean score than the first batsman but has a much smaller range, showing that he is more consistent.

Total score = Mean score × Number of innings
= 60 × 6
= 360

EXERCISE 9.2

1. For each of the following sets of numbers find the mean, mode, median and range.
    (i) 5, 7, 5, 3, 7, 9, 5, 4, 8
    (ii) 13, 19, 24, 32, 34, 39, 60, 70
    (iii) 5, 14, 8, 11, 8, 8, 2

2. The lowest temperatures in °C recorded over a 10-day period were as follows:
    15, 11, 10, 10, 13, 16, 14, 10, 15, 9
    Find the modal, mean and median temperatures, and the temperature range over this period.

3. Five members of a family had the following jobs and salaries:

Pilot   £55 000
Lecturer   £20 000
Engineer   £18 000
Secretary   £12 000
Shop assistant   £10 000

Find the mean and median salary of the household. Which of the answers, in your opinion, is the best one to represent the five salaries?

4. The bar chart in Fig. 9.12 shows the daily sales over a 6-day period of a CD topping the chart.

Find   (i) the mean sales per day
        (ii) the range of the sales figures per day
       (iii) the mode value of the sales

Fig. 9.12

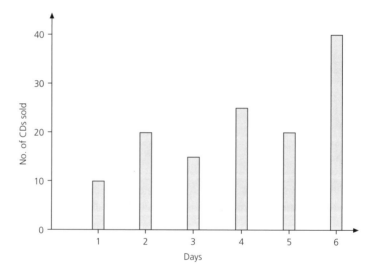

5. The ages, in years, of 16 employees in a building firm are

17, 18, 20, 21, 25, 26, 27, 28, 32, 33, 35, 38, 41, 42, 47, 49

What is (i) the mean, mode and median ages of the employees?
          (ii) the age range of the employees?

6. The mean annual wage for 8 craftsmen is £16 000. What is the total annual wage bill for these craftsmen?

7. A group of 5 people have a mean height of 1.74 m. If another person of height 1.83 m joins the group, what is the average height of the 6 people?

8. A batsman has an average of 48 runs per innings over the previous 9 innings. How many runs would he have to score in his next innings to change his average to 50 runs?

9. The money spent per week by two motorists was recorded for a period of 4 weeks as shown.

Motorist A	£6.86	£10.80	£21.24	£18.42
Motorist B	£15.66	£13.94	£15.08	£12.52

Find the mean sum spent per week and the range for each motorist. Compare the two sets of expenditure.

10. The table below shows the number of electrical appliances sold each week by 2 salesmen over a 6-week period.

Week	1	2	3	4	5	6
Salesman 1	30	89	49	93	60	101
Salesman 2	73	61	84	47	70	45

Find the mean and range for both salesmen and compare their performances.

10 Further arithmetic methods

10.1 Ratio

In chapter 3 a method was shown how to divide up a quantity according to a given ratio, such as dividing £30 in a ratio 2:3. The first step is always to consider the ratio as a number of parts, that is, $2 + 3 = 5$ parts.

A different problem is now looked at, where we work back from knowing the value of one part of the ratio to find the original quantity. For example, a load of sand for a play area was divided into two piles, in the ratio 4:7, that is, 4 parts to 7 parts. The smaller of the two piles weighed 20 kg. From this information can be calculated the weight of the original load.

$$\begin{aligned}
&4 \text{ parts weigh} & &20 \text{ kg} \\
&1 \text{ part weighs} & &20 \div 4 = 5 \text{ kg} \\
&7 \text{ parts weigh} & &5 \times 7 \ \ = 35 \text{ kg}
\end{aligned}$$

The original load weighed $20 + 35 = 55$ kg.

EXAMPLE 10.1

A garden was divided into a lawn and a vegetable patch in the ratio 5:7. The lawn has an area of 30 m^2. Calculate the area of the vegetable patch and the size of the whole garden.

Solution

The garden can be divided up into $5 + 7$ parts, 5 parts being lawn and 7 parts being vegetables.

Writing out the statements:

$$\begin{aligned}
&\text{The lawn of 5 parts is } 30 \text{ m}^2 \\
&1 \text{ part is } 30 \div 5 = \ \ 6 \text{ m}^2 \\
&7 \text{ parts is } \ \ 6 \times 7 = 42 \text{ m}^2 \\
&\text{Area of vegetable patch} = 42 \text{ m}^2 \\
&\text{The whole garden has an area of } 30 + 42 = 72 \text{ m}^2
\end{aligned}$$

EXAMPLE 10.2

In a superstore the numbers of supervisors, cleaners and checkout staff are in the ratio 2:3:7. If the number of supervisors is 10, what is the number of each of the other staff?

Solution

Of the total, 2 parts of the staff are supervisors, 3 parts are cleaners, 7 parts are checkout staff.

Supervisors: 2 parts = 10 staff
Therefore 1 part = 10 ÷ 2 = 5 staff

Cleaners: 3 parts = 5 × 3 = 15 staff
Checkout: 7 parts = 5 × 7 = 35 staff

Total staff in the store = 10 + 15 + 35
= 60

EXERCISE 10.1

1. Ordinary brass contains zinc and copper in the ratio 2:3. 12 tonnes of zinc are placed in the furnace. How many tonnes of copper will be required to make the brass?

2. Three partners in a solicitors' practice invested money in the ratio 6:8:10. Find (i) the simplest form of the ratio, (ii) the total sum invested if the partner with the smallest ratio invested £15 000.

3. A hot drink is made up of whisky and water in the ratio 3:5. How much whisky is added to 20 c*l* of water?

4. A trainee on work placement received an allowance of £15 a week. The ratio between his allowance and the wage of an apprentice was 3:8.
    How much was the apprentice paid each week?

5. A contractor costing a job uses a ratio 12:10 for labour and materials respectively. If the cost of materials was estimated to be £420, what was the estimate for the total cost of the job?

6. Two people in a syndicate share the prize in a lottery draw in the ratio 7:4. If the larger share was £28 000, what was the other share?

7. The White Lady cocktail contains gin, lemon juice and Cointreau in the ratio 2:1:1. To make this cocktail for a party the barman used 120 m*l* of gin. What was the total volume of the cocktail? If this was served in 60 m*l* glasses, how many glasses would it serve?

8. Two pieces of a wooden rod are required in the ratio 5:7. If the smaller piece is to be 2 m in length, what will be the length of the other piece?

9. A floor cleaner must be diluted with water in the ratio 1 part cleaner to 20 parts water. If 7 ml of floor cleaner was added to 100 ml of water, how much more water is required to produce the right concentration?

10. In a factory the wages of women to men were in the ratio 3:4. If the women received a basic wage of £9000, what wages should they receive to satisfy the Equal Opportunities Commission?

11. The estimated costs for materials and labour for a kitchen conversion were in the ratio 4:5. The labour cost was set at £800. What was the total estimate for the job? However, it was found that owing to delays the labour costs increased in the ratio 3:2 and materials increased in the ratio 7:5. What was the actual cost of conversion?

12. Three grades of staff in a company receive salaries in the ratio 3:4:5. The difference between the top grade and the bottom grade is £5000. What is each grade paid?

10.2 Inverse proportion

In chapter 3 calculations were considered where one quantity was always in direct proportion to another. However, there are quantities that are in inverse or indirect proportion to one another. This is the case when an increase in one quantity produces a decrease in the other in the same ratio. This is shown in the following examples.

EXAMPLE 10.3

A company has estimated that an order for a customer would take 20 days to complete with 12 machines working. However, the customer insists on delivery in 16 days. How many machines would need to be working to meet the new deadline?

Solution

To *reduce* the length of time to complete the order an *increase* is required in the number of machines working, so that the proportion is indirect. Writing out the statements:

  12 machines working complete the order in 20 days
  ? machines working complete the order in 16 days

The numbers of days are in the ratio 16:20, that is, $\frac{16}{20}$.

The numbers of machines are in the inverse ratio, that is, $\frac{20}{16}$.

The number of working machines required is $12 \times \frac{20}{16} = 15$.

A familiar example of inverse proportion occurs when making car journeys. Increasing the speed of travelling reduces the time taken, so that speed and time are in inverse proportion. This is shown in the following example.

EXAMPLE 10.4

The journey between two places takes 5 hours on the motorway when the average speed of the car is 63 mph. (i) How long would the journey take at a speed of 45 mph? (ii) At what speed must the car travel to cover the journey in 4 hours?

Solution

(i) Writing out the two statements:

Journey time is 5 hours at a speed of 63 mph
Journey time is ? hours at a speed of 45 mph

The speeds are in the ratio 45:63, that is, $\frac{45}{63}$.

The journey times are in the inverse ratio, that is, $\frac{63}{45}$.

The new journey time is $5 \times \frac{63}{45} = 7$ hours.

(ii) Writing out the two statements:

Journey time is 5 hours at a speed of 63 mph
Journey time is 4 hours at a speed of   ? mph

The journey times are in the ratio 4:5, that is, $\frac{4}{5}$.

The speeds to achieve this are in the inverse ratio, that is, $\frac{5}{4}$.

The new speed is a $\frac{5}{4} \times 63 = 78\frac{3}{4}$ mph.

EXERCISE 10.2

1. A train travelling at 120 mph covered a journey from London in 5 hours. On the return journey the speed was reduced to 90 mph. How long did the return journey take?

2. A mother buys a supply of cereals which lasts her 3 children for 14 days. When 4 cousins come to stay, how long will the same supply of cereals now last?

3. At a supermarket, 24 people restock the shelves overnight in 6 hours. How many people would be required to restock the shelves in 8 hours?

4. A contractor estimates that he can build a certain number of houses in 48 weeks using 25 men. Because of bad weather he needs to complete them in 40 weeks. How many men will he need to complete the work in the shorter time?

5. A County Council has set aside a fixed budget for repair and maintenance of its houses. At an average cost of £1200 per house it was estimated that they could

repair 180 houses. However, the actual cost was found to be £1500 per house. How many houses could be repaired from the agreed budget?

6. A company received an order for a special piece of equipment. Using 15 men it can be made in 10 days. However, the customer insists on delivery within 6 days. How many more men will be needed?

10.3 Percentage

In calculations dealing with value added tax (VAT), profit, investments etc. a percentage is added to an original sum of money to obtain the final amount. The calculation may be occur in two ways.

(i) The original sum of money is known and a percentage of this amount is added to produce the final sum of money. This type of problem was dealt with in chapter 4, and is summarised in Fig. 10.1(a).

(ii) The final sum of money is known and the original sum needs to be calculated. The difficulty is that the percentage increase needs to be calculated on the original sum, which is not known. This is illustrated in Fig. 10.1(b).

Consider the addition of 5% VAT on electricity bills.

Fig. 10.1

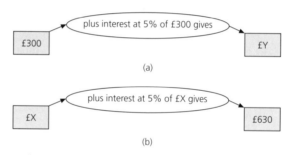

(i) In Fig. 10.1(a) VAT at 5% is added to an electricity charge of £300, and the final bill £Y has to be calculated.

If we start with an electricity charge of £100 we know that VAT at 5% will make a final bill of £105. Writing out the two statements:

A charge of £100 plus VAT at 5% gives a final bill of £105
A charge of £300 plus VAT at 5% gives a final bill of   ?

The electricity charges are in the ratio $\frac{300}{100}$.

The final bills will be in the same ratio, that is $\frac{300}{100}$.

The final bill, charges + VAT = $\frac{300}{100} \times 105$

which can be written as $= 300 \times 1.05$

$= £315$

Therefore it can be seen that

Final bill = Original charge $\times$ 1.05.

(ii) In Fig. 10.1(b) the final bill is £630 which includes VAT at 5%. However, the VAT is 5% of the original sum £X and X is to be calculated.

Again we start with an electricity charge of £100 and writing out the two statements:

£105 is the final bill for an original charge of £100
£630 is the final bill for an original charge of ?

The final bills are in the ratio $\frac{630}{105}$

The original charges are in the same ratio $\frac{630}{105}$

The original charge $= \frac{630}{105} \times 100$

which can be written as $= \frac{630}{1.05}$

$= £600$

It can be seen that the original charge is given by

Original charge = Final bill ÷ 1.05

The two rules can be summarised in Fig. 10.2.

Fig. 10.2

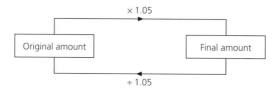

In Fig. 10.2 the increase caused by VAT at 5% gave a factor of 1.05. With VAT at 17.5% the factor becomes 1.175. Similarly, if goods were sold at a profit of 15% the factor would be 1.15.

This rule, with the percentage increase changed to the appropriate factor, is used in Examples 10.5 and 10.6.

EXAMPLE 10.5

A sum of money was invested at 10% annual rate of interest. After 1 year the total invested was £385. What was the original sum invested?

Solution

The problem is illustrated in Fig. 10.3.

Fig. 10.3

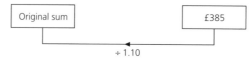

The annual rate of interest of 10% gives a factor of 1.10.
Therefore original sum = £385 ÷ 1.1 = £350

EXAMPLE 10.6

In a garage the total bill for repairs was £141, including VAT at 17.5%. What was the repair charge before VAT was added?

Solution

Using Fig. 10.2 with VAT at 17.5%,

actual repair charge before VAT was added = £141 ÷ 1.175 = £120

EXERCISE 10.3

1. A holiday to the Costa Brava cost a family £1410 including VAT at 17.5%. What was the cost excluding VAT?

2. A meal in a restaurant costs £47 including VAT at 17.5%. How much was the meal excluding VAT?

3. A shopkeeper sold a hairdrier for £36, excluding VAT, making a profit of 20%. What was the original price paid by the shopkeeper?

4. Clothes in a dress shop were sold at $33\frac{1}{3}$% profit. A lady spent £120 on children's clothes, which are VAT free. How much was the profit to the dress shop owner?

5. A student spent £2.35 in a fish and chip restaurant. With VAT at 17.5%, how much did the owner receive from this sum?

6. A computer is sold for £940 including VAT at 17.5%. What was the selling price excluding VAT? If the store owner made 20% profit, how much did he originally pay for the computer?

10.4 Money

Compound interest

In previous chapters calculations were carried out to find the simple interest on sums of money deposited in banks and building societies. Such calculations apply to the special situation when the interest is withdrawn each year. In practice the interest is usually added to the capital sum deposited. The interest will be now be on this new sum, and is called the *compound interest*.

The calculation of compound interest is shown in Example 10.7.

EXAMPLE 10.7

Calculate the increase in the sum of £200 deposited in a building society for 3 years if the rate of compound interest is 8% per year.

> *Solution*
>
> Beginning of 1st year : sum deposited : £200.00
> Interest in 1st year   : 8% of £200   : <u>£16.00</u>
> End of 1st year   : total sum   : £216.00
> Interest in 2nd year   : 8% of £216   : <u>£17.28</u>
> End of 2nd year   : total sum   : £233.28
> Interest in 3rd year   : 8% of £233.28 : <u>£18.6624</u>
> End of 3rd year   : total sum   : £251.9424
>
> After 3 years the sum has risen to £251.94, correct to the nearest penny.
> Increase = total interest earned = £251.94 − £200 = £51.94

Electricity, gas and telephone bills

Electricity and telephone bills are sent to customers every 3 months.

Electricity and gas bills
The electricity bill is made up of three parts:

- a fixed service or standing charge, which does not depend on the amount of electricity or gas used
- the charge for the units of electricity or gas used
- VAT at 5%

A typical bill is shown in Example 10.8.

EXAMPLE 10.8

Find the total amount due for payment on the quarterly bill shown below.

Electricity plc   CUSTOMER ACCOUNT

Meter Readings

Previous	Present	Units used	Cost : 7p per unit	£
17 381	18 936	?	? @ 7p Service Charge	? 10.50
			Total Electricity Charges VAT at 5%	? ?
			AMOUNT DUE	?

Solution

The number of units used is 18 936 − 17 381

$$\frac{\begin{array}{r} 18\ 936 \\ 17\ 381 \end{array}}{1\ 555}$$

Charge for units used 1555 × 7p

$$\frac{\times\quad 7}{10885\text{p}} = £108.85$$

Total electricity charges = £108.85 + £10.50 = £119.35
VAT at 5% = 5% of £119.35 = £5.97
TOTAL AMOUNT = £125.32

The complete invoice is

Electricity plc		CUSTOMER ACCOUNT		
Meter Readings				
Previous	Present	Units used	Cost : 7p per unit	£
17 381	18 936	1555	1555 @ 7p	108.85
			Service Charge	10.50
			Total Electricity Charges	119.35
			VAT at 5%	5.97
			AMOUNT DUE	125.32

Telephone bill

A telephone bill consists of:

- call charges for the previous three months
- call discounts
- advanced charges including rental for the next three months
- VAT at 17.5%

A telephone bill is shown below:

BT

Phone bill

£	100.33	Call charges
		£95.20 for direct dialled calls
		£5.13 for Network Services calls
£	−14.50	Call Discounts/Allowances
£	85.83	Subtotal including discount
£	31.55	Advanced charges
£	117.38	Subtotal excluding VAT
£	20.54	VAT at 17.5%
£	**137.92**	**Total amount due**

EXERCISE 10.4

1. Find the total amount in an account after 2 years if £200 were deposited at a compound annual interest of 5%.

2. £1000 was placed into a building society, paying annual interest at 6%. Find the total compound interest after 3 years.

3. £400 was deposited in a savings account at an annual rate of 5%. After 4 years what is (i) the compound interest, (ii) the total simple interest?

4. Complete the following electricity bill by filling in the shaded boxes.

CUSTOMER ACCOUNT			**Energy One**	
Meter Readings				
Previous	Present	Units used	Cost : 7p per unit	£
5314	6005	[ ]	[ ] @ 7p	[ ]
			Service Charge	12.50
			Total electricity charges	[ ]
			VAT at 5%	[ ]
			AMOUNT DUE	[ ]

5. Complete the following telephone bill by filling in the shaded boxes.

BT

Phone bill

£	▢	Call charges £40.18 for direct dialled calls £2.31 for Network Services calls
£	−4.20	Call Discounts/Allowances
	▢	Subtotal including discounts
£	32.00	Advance charge
£	▢	Subtotal excluding VAT
£	▢	VAT at 17.5%
£	▢	**Total amount due**

6. A gas bill contained the following details:
units used 170, cost per unit 45p, standing charge £16.20
Calculate (i) the total charge for gas excluding VAT, (ii) the final bill if VAT is 5%.

10.5 Compound units of measurement

In chapter 5 the units of length, weight and volume (capacity) were listed and used, that is,

length: metre (m)
weight: kilogram (kg)
capacity: cubic metre (m^3)

together with their subunits.
From these units it is possible to create other units for practical quantities such as

speed: metres per second (m/s), kilometres per hour (km/h)
flow of water: cubic metres per second (m^3/s)
density: kilograms per cubic metre (kg/m^3)

These units are called *compound units*.

Speed

Speed is the distance travelled in one unit of time, that is, 1 hour or 1 second. Consider a car which travels 300 km in 6 hours at a steady speed.

In 6 hours the car travelled 300 km
In 1 hour the car travelled 300 ÷ 6 = 50 km

The speed of the car is the number of kilometres travelled in 1 hour.

Speed of car = 50 km/h

Therefore speed is obtained by dividing the distance travelled by the time taken.

$$\text{Speed} = \frac{\text{Distance}}{\text{Time}}$$

The units of speed are km/h, m/s and miles per hour (mph).

EXAMPLE 10.9

A train travels 600 km in 4 hours. What is the speed of the train in metres per second (m/s)?

Solution

In this case the distance needs to be in metres (m) and the time in seconds (s).

Distance = 600 km = 600 × 1000 m
Time = 4 h   = 4 × 3600 s

where 3600 is the number of seconds in an hour.

$$\text{Speed} = \frac{600 \times 1000}{4 \times 3600} = 42 \text{ m/s to 2 significant figures}$$

Rate of flow of water in a pipe

This is another example of a compound measure since rate of flow is the volume flowing per second.

Let 50 *l* of water flow through a pipe in 10 s.

In 10 s quantity of water flowing = 50 *l*
In 1 s quantity of water flowing = 50 ÷ 10 = 5 *l*

The rate of flow = 5 *l*/s

$$\text{Rate of flow} = \frac{\text{Volume}}{\text{Time}}$$

The units of rate of flow are *l*/s and m³/s.

EXAMPLE 10.10

A volume of 450 m³ flows though a pipeline in 5 minutes. What is the rate of flow in *l*/s?

Solution

$$\text{Volume} = 450 \text{ m}^3 \qquad = 450 \times 1000 \; l$$
$$\text{Time} = 5 \text{ min} \qquad = 300 \text{ s}$$
$$\text{Rate of flow} = \frac{450 \times 1000}{300} = 1500 \; l/s$$

Density

In order to compare how heavy different substances are it is necessary to compare weights of a same basic volume for each substance. This volume is taken as 1 m*l*, 1 litre, or 1 m³. The weight of such a volume is called the density. For example

30 m*l* of alcohol weighs 24 g
1 m*l* of alcohol weighs 24 ÷ 30 = 0.8 g

Density is the weight of 1 m*l*, so that the density of alcohol is 0.8 g/m*l*.
From this calculation it is seen that

$$\text{Density} = \frac{\text{Weight}}{\text{Volume}}$$

The various units of density are g/m*l*, g/*l* and kg/m³.

EXAMPLE 10.11

A solid gold cube of sides of 3 cm weighs 521 g. What is the density of gold?

Solution

Volume of cube = 3 × 3 × 3 = 27 cm³
Weight of cube = 521 g

Using the above formula

Density of gold = $\frac{521}{27}$ = 19.3 g/cm³

Fuel consumption

A familiar compound unit is the number of miles or kilometres a car will travel for each gallon or litre of petrol. Consider an example of a car travelling 240 miles using 6 gallons of petrol.

With 6 gallons the car travels 240 miles
With 1 gallon the car travels 240 ÷ 6 = 40 miles

The rating of petrol consumption is then 40 miles/gal.
The formula for petrol consumption is

$$\text{Fuel consumption} = \frac{\text{Distance}}{\text{Volume (of fuel)}}$$

The units of fuel consumption are km/l and miles/gal (mpg).

1. A sprinter runs 100 m in 10 s. What is his speed over this distance in (i) metres per second, (ii) kilometres per hour?

2. A storage tank of capacity 20 000 gal is full of oil. It is emptied in 4 h. What is the rate of discharge of oil in gal/h and gal/min?

3. A car will travel 480 km on 60 litres of petrol. What is the rate of petrol consumption (i) in km/l and (ii) mpg?

4. A solid cube of sides 5.0 cm weighed 1.125 kg. Calculate the density in g/cm^3 and kg/m^3.

5. A 5.0 m^3 tank is filled with water in 25 min. What is the rate of flow in (i) m^3/min, (ii) l/s?

6. The density of water is 1 g/ml. What is the density of water in kg/m^3?

7. A rectangular tank 0.8 m × 1.8 m × 1.2 m is full of oil. If the oil weighs 1.6 tonnes, what is the density of oil in kg/m^3?

8. The densities of two materials are 1090 kg/m^3 and 7600 kg/m^3. If the two materials are steel and polythene, which of the two values is the density of polythene?

9. Two cars have fuel consumptions of 35 mpg and 12 km/litre. Which car has the better consumption?

10. A car is travelling at 22 m/s. What is the speed in km/h?

10.6 Errors

Errors in measurement

In chapter 2 accuracy in numbers was related to significant figures. Numbers are terminated to a given number of significant figures as determined by the level of accuracy required. When such numbers refer to actual measurements with instruments or rulers, however, the accuracy is determined by the measuring instruments. Measurements are made using marked scales which have been calibrated to correspond to the units of length, capacity etc. The simplest and most familiar measuring instrument is the ruler which is marked in centimetres or inches.

Fig. 10.4

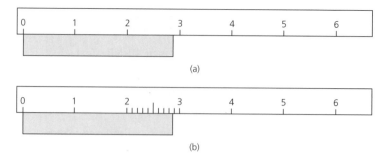

Consider the shaded length of wood shown in Fig. 10.4, which is being measured by two rulers, one marked in centimetres only, the other marked in centimetres and millimetres.

In Fig. 10.4(a) the shaded length of wood lies between 2 and 3 cm. Because there are no marks on the ruler between 2 and 3, the length can only be estimated as 2.9 cm. It is accurate to the nearest 0.1 cm.

In Fig. 10.4(b) the length of the same piece of wood can be read more accurately, where it can be seen to be between 2.8 and 2.9 cm long. The length can now be estimated as 2.86 cm. It is now accurate to the nearest 0.01 cm.

This is illustrated further in the measurement of temperature.

In Fig. 10.5 (a) the thermometer is graduated into 5° steps. The temperature can only be estimated as 34 °C, that is to the nearest degree Celsius.

Fig. 10.5

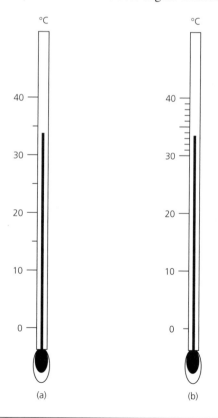

By using a more accurate thermometer, marked in steps of 1 °C as in Fig. 10.5(b), the temperature can be estimated as 33.5 °C.

From these two examples it can be seen that the more accurate the measuring instrument, the more accurately the reading can be expressed. In so doing the number of significant figures is increased.

Therefore the aim is to make more accurate measuring instruments, but the last significant figure will always have an inaccuracy reflecting the limitation of the equipment.

EXAMPLE 10.12

What is the volume of liquid in the measuring cylinder shown in Fig. 10.6? What is the accuracy of the reading?

Fig. 10.6

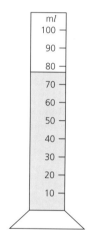

Solution

The measuring cylinder is marked in 10 m*l* steps. The volume of liquid lies between 70 and 80 m*l*. It is possible to estimate the volume to the nearest 1 m*l* between the graduations, that is

volume = 77 m*l*

The volume is estimated to 2 significant figures. It is correct to the nearest 1 m*l*.

EXERCISE 10.6

1. What are the volumes in each of the cylinders in Fig. 10.7, giving the level of accuracy in each case?

Fig. 10.7

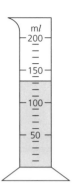

2. The ruler in Fig. 10.8 is graduated in centimetres. What is the length of the rod AB, stating the level of accuracy?

Fig. 10.8

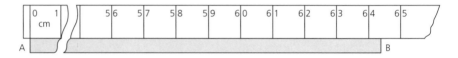

3. In the ruler in Fig. 10.9 the numbers are centimetres, and the subdivisions are in millimetres. What is the length of the rod AB and its level of accuracy?

Fig. 10.9

4. Fig. 10.10 shows a meter for measuring electric current in amperes. What is the meter reading, stating its accuracy?

Fig. 10.10

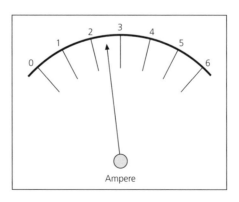

5. Fig. 10.11 shows a pressure gauge reading of air pressure in a tyre of a lorry. What is the pressure reading, stating its accuracy level?

Fig. 10.11

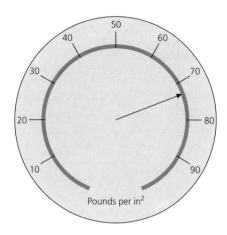

Errors in calculating

In Fig. 10.12 it can be seen that a rod of length 30 cm which is rounded to 2 significant figures has

a smallest possible length = 29.5 cm
a greatest possible length = 30.5 cm

Fig. 10.12

Rounded off in this way means that the length is accurate to the nearest 1 cm.
Consider three rods 30 cm long laid out end to end as shown in Fig. 10.13.

Fig. 10.13

Using the rounded length we could say that the

total length of the three rods = 90 cm

Since it is rounded to 2 significant figures, this suggests that the total length lies between 89.5 and 90.5 cm. However,

the smallest possible total length of the 3 rods = 3 × 29.5 = 88.5 cm
the greatest possible total length of the 3 rods = 3 × 30.5 = 91.5 cm

This means that the result of 90 cm can have an error up to ±1.5 cm.

This shows that errors may accumulate as a calculation proceeds and that an answer may not be as accurate as the number suggests.

Consider another example of this in Example 10.13.

EXAMPLE 10.13

A metal plate has a length of 44 cm and width of 36 cm. Find the smallest and greatest possible values of the area and give the area of the plate to an appropriate degree of accuracy.

Solution

Using the given figures

$$\text{Area} = 44 \times 36 = 1584 \text{ cm}^2$$

However, since both length and width are given to 2 significant figures

Smallest possible length = 43.5 cm
Smallest possible width = 35.5 cm
Smallest possible area   = $43.5 \times 35.5 = 1544.25$ cm^2

Greatest possible length = 44.5 cm
Greatest possible width = 36.5 cm
Greatest possible area   = $44.5 \times 36.5 = 1624.25$ cm^2.

Since the answer of 1584 cm^2 could be in error of up to ±40 cm^2 it is misleading to give the answer to 4 significant figures, because the last two figures are incorrect. It is more realistic to express the answer as

Area of plate = 1600 cm^2 correct to 2 significant figures

RULE

The result of any calculation should be expressed to the same number of significant figures as that of the least accurate data. However, if the result of this calculation is to be used in a further calculation, it should be used with one more significant figure.

EXERCISE 10.7

1. A length and width of a sheet of paper, rounded to 2 significant figures, are 22 cm and 15 cm. Find the smallest and greatest possible length and width.

2. Calculate the smallest and greatest possible areas of the sheet of paper in Question 1 and express the area to a suitable number of significant figures.

3. A chemical compound is weighed and found to be 1650 mg, rounded to 3 significant figures. What are the smallest and the greatest possible weights of the compound?

4. Five pieces of plywood each of which measures 62 cm × 43 cm, rounded to 2 significant figures, are joined together as shown in Fig. 10.14. What is the smallest and greatest possible length and width of the layout?

Fig. 10.14

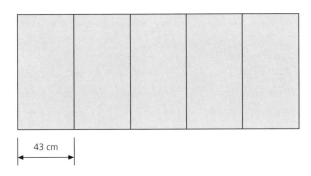

43 cm

5. Two sheets of cardboard having dimensions 20 cm by 11 cm, rounded to 2 significant figures, are joined together as shown in Fig. 10.15.

Fig. 10.15

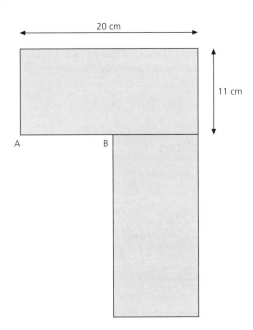

20 cm

11 cm

A   B

Find the least and greatest length of AB.

6. A cup can hold 210 ml of water correct to 2 significant figures. What is the least number of cupfuls needed to fill a bucket which has a capacity of 5.2 litres, correct to 2 significant figures?

7. Small boxes with a cubical shape have a side 6.2 cm. What is the greatest number of boxes that can fit into the length of a large box 74 cm long?

11 Formulae and graphs II

11.1 Indices

The multiplication and division of numbers in the form of indices has already been explained in chapter 1, that is

$$5^3 \times 5^4 = 5^{3+4} = 5^7$$

The indices are added, provided the numbers have a common base, such as 5 in this example.

Similarly, division is carried out by subtracting indices

$$8^6 \div 8^4 = 8^{6-4} = 8^2$$

The meaning of negative and fractional indices is now considered.

Negative indices

Using the rule for division

$$7^3 \div 7^5 = 7^{3-5} = 7^{-2}$$

But

$$7^3 \div 7^5 = \frac{7 \times 7 \times 7}{7 \times 7 \times 7 \times 7 \times 7} = \frac{1}{7^2}$$

Therefore

$$7^{-2} = \frac{1}{7^2}$$

A negative index means that the number is inverted.

EXAMPLE 11.1

Convert the following numbers to positive indices:

(i) 8^{-3} (ii) 10^{-5} (iii) $\dfrac{1}{6^{-2}}$ (iv) $\dfrac{1}{4^{-2}}$

(i) $8^{-3} = \dfrac{1}{8^3}$

(ii) $10^{-5} = \dfrac{1}{10^5}$

(iii) In this case the number is inverted from the bottom line (denominator) to the top line (numerator):

$$\dfrac{1}{6^{-2}} = 6^2$$

(iv) $\dfrac{1}{4^{-2}} = 4^2$

EXAMPLE 11.2

Write the following with positive indices and work out their values.

(i) 2^{-3} (ii) 4^{-1} (iii) $\dfrac{1}{3^{-3}}$

Solution

(i) $2^{-3} = \dfrac{1}{2^3} = \dfrac{1}{2 \times 2 \times 2} = \dfrac{1}{8}$

(ii) $4^{-1} = \dfrac{1}{4^1} = \dfrac{1}{4}$

(iii) $\dfrac{1}{3^{-3}} = 3^3 = 3 \times 3 \times 3 = 27$

Fractional indices

In order to find out what a fractional index means, the square root of a number is first considered.

Since $\sqrt{9} = 3$,

$$\sqrt{9} \times \sqrt{9} = 3 \times 3 = 9$$

From the first rule of indices for the multiplication of numbers in index form

$$9^{\frac{1}{2}} \times 9^{\frac{1}{2}} = 9^1 = 9$$

From these two results $9^{\frac{1}{2}} = \sqrt{9}$

The result shows that an index of $\frac{1}{2}$ means the square root of the number. Similarly an index of $\frac{1}{3}$ means the cube root of a number, that is

$$8^{\frac{1}{3}} = \sqrt[3]{8}$$

EXAMPLE 11.3

Find the value of (i) $25^{\frac{1}{2}}$, (ii) $4^{\frac{1}{2}}$, (iii) $8^{\frac{1}{3}}$, (iv) $16^{-\frac{1}{2}}$.

Solution

(i) $25^{\frac{1}{2}} = \sqrt{25} = 5$

(ii) $4^{\frac{1}{2}} = \sqrt{4} = 2$

(iii) $8^{\frac{1}{3}} = \sqrt[3]{8} = 2$ since $8 = 2 \times 2 \times 2$

(iv) $16^{-\frac{1}{2}} = \dfrac{1}{16^{\frac{1}{2}}} = \dfrac{1}{\sqrt{16}} = \dfrac{1}{4}$

Combined indices

In an expression such as $(2^3)^2$ there are 2 indices with one base number. This can be written as $2^3 \times 2^3$ and the rule of multiplication applied, that is

$$2^3 \times 2^3 = 2^{3+3} = 2^6$$

This result can be obtained by multiplying the two indices

$$(2^3)^2 = 2^{3 \times 2} = 2^6$$

This method can be used for numbers with combined indices as shown below:

$$(10^3)^2 = 10^{3 \times 2} = 10^6$$
$$(2^4)^{\frac{1}{2}} = 2^{4 \times \frac{1}{2}} = 2^2 = 4$$

EXAMPLE 11.4

Simplify the following using the method of indices.

(i) $16^{\frac{1}{2}}$ (ii) $64^{\frac{1}{3}}$ (iii) $\left(\dfrac{9}{16}\right)^{\frac{1}{2}}$ (iv) $\left(\dfrac{1}{9}\right)^{-\frac{1}{2}}$

(v) $(10^{-1})^2$ (vi) $8^{\frac{2}{3}}$ (vii) $\left(\dfrac{25}{16}\right)^{-\frac{3}{2}}$

> **Solution**
>
> (i) $16^{\frac{1}{2}} = \sqrt{16} = 4$
>
> (ii) $64^{\frac{1}{3}} = \sqrt[3]{64} = 4$
>
> (iii) $\left(\dfrac{9}{16}\right)^{\frac{1}{2}} = \dfrac{3}{4}$
>
> (iv) The index is converted into $+\frac{1}{2}$ by inverting the fraction, that is
>
> $\left(\dfrac{1}{9}\right)^{-\frac{1}{2}} = \left(\dfrac{9}{1}\right)^{\frac{1}{2}} = 3$
>
> (v) $(10^{-1})^2 = \left(\dfrac{1}{10}\right)^2 = \dfrac{1}{100}$
>
> (vi) $8^{\frac{2}{3}} = \left(8^{\frac{1}{3}}\right)^2 = (2)^2 = 4$
>
> (vii) $\left(\dfrac{25}{16}\right)^{-\frac{3}{2}} = \left(\dfrac{16}{25}\right)^{\frac{3}{2}} = \dfrac{\left(16^{\frac{1}{2}}\right)^3}{\left(25^{\frac{1}{2}}\right)^3} = \left(\dfrac{4}{5}\right)^3 = \dfrac{64}{125}$

EXERCISE 11.1

1. Using the rules of indices work out the following, leaving your answers in the form of indices.

   (i) $6^4 \times 6^5$ (ii) $10^4 \times 10^{-3}$ (iii) $5^{-3} \times 5^{-2}$ (iv) $5^{\frac{1}{2}} \times 5^{\frac{3}{2}}$ (v) $7^5 \div 7^3$
   (vi) $8^6 \div 8^9$ (vii) $5^{-2} \div 5^{-7}$ (viii) $3^8 \div 3^8$ (ix) $(10^2)^4$

2. Write the following with positive indices.

   (i) 8^{-2} (ii) 6^{-1} (iii) 10^{-2} (iv) $\dfrac{1}{7^{-6}}$ (v) $\dfrac{1}{10^{-3}}$

3. Work out the following.

   (i) $16^{\frac{1}{4}}$ (ii) $625^{\frac{1}{2}}$ (iii) $81^{\frac{3}{2}}$ (iv) $32^{\frac{2}{5}}$

   (v) $27^{-\frac{1}{3}}$ (vi) $\left(\dfrac{1}{4}\right)^{-\frac{5}{2}}$ (vii) $\left(\dfrac{32}{243}\right)^{-\frac{1}{5}}$

11.2 Numbers in standard form

Very large or very small numbers cannot be entered into a calculator if they consist of too many digits. In such cases the numbers are first written in *standard form*. Numbers in standard form are written as a decimal number between 1 and 10, multiplied by multiples or sub-multiples of 10, expressed in index form, such as, for example, 7.36×10^4.

(i) For large numbers the decimal point is shifted BACK and placed after the first significant figure. In order to keep the value the same the number must then be multiplied by 10 to an index equal to the number of places the decimal point has been shifted.

$6\,3\,7\,.\,5 = 6.375 \times 100 = 6.375 \times 10^2$
(shifting the decimal point 2 places to the **left** and multiplying by 10^2)

$7\,3\,9\,1 = 7.391 \times 1000 = 7.391 \times 10^3$
(shifting the decimal point 3 places to the **left** and multiplying by 10^3)

$43\,970\,000 = 4.397 \times 10^7$
(shifting the decimal point 7 places to the left and multiplying by 10^7)

(ii) For very small numbers the decimal point is shifted FORWARD and placed after the first significant figure. In order to keep the value the same the number must then be divided by 10 to the index equal to the number of places the decimal point has been shifted.

$$0.0\,5\,7\,2 = \frac{5.72}{100} = \frac{5.72}{10^2} = 5.72 \times 10^{-2}$$

(shifting the decimal point 2 places to the **right** and dividing by 10^2)

Again

$$0.0\,0\,0\,2\,5\,9 = \frac{2.59}{10\,000} = \frac{2.59}{10^4} = 2.59 \times 10^{-4}$$

Example 11.5 shows how numbers in standard form can be changed back into ordinary form.

EXAMPLE 11.5

Write the following numbers in ordinary form.

(i) 3.72×10^5 (ii) 3.0×10^6 (iii) 4.135×10^{-6} (iv) 3.3×10^{-2}

Solution

(i) Multiplying by 10^5 means shifting the decimal point 5 places to the right.
   $3.72 \times 10^5 = 3.72 \times 100\,000 = 372\,000$

(ii) $3.0 \times 10^6 = 3.0 \times 1\,000\,000 = 3\,000\,000$

(iii) Multiplying by 10^{-6} means shifting the decimal point 6 places to the left.
   $4.135 \times 10^{-6} = 4.135 \div 10^6 = 0.000\,004\,135$

(iv) $3.3 \times 10^{-2} = 0.033$

Numbers in standard form can be multiplied and divided using the rules of indices as shown in Example 11.6.

EXAMPLE 11.6

Evaluate the following.

(i) $3.1 \times 10^3 \times 2 \times 10^5$ (ii) $4.8 \times 10^{-6} \div (1.2 \times 10^{-4})$

(iii) $\dfrac{6.3 \times 10^8 \times 4.4 \times 10^{-4}}{9.9 \times 10^{-3} \times 2.1 \times 10^5}$

Solution

(i) Numbers in index form are multiplied by adding the indices:

$$3.1 \times 10^3 \times 2 \times 10^5 = 3.1 \times 2 \times 10^{3+5}$$
$$= 6.2 \times 10^8$$

(ii) Numbers in index form are divided by subtracting the indices:

$$4.8 \times 10^{-6} \div (1.2 \times 10^{-4}) = \frac{4.8}{1.2} \times 10^{-6-(-4)}$$
$$= 4.0 \times 10^{-6+4}$$
$$= 4.0 \times 10^{-2}$$

(iii) $\dfrac{6.3 \times 10^8 \times 4.4 \times 10^{-4}}{9.9 \times 10^{-3} \times 2.1 \times 10^5} = \dfrac{\overset{3}{6.3} \times \overset{4}{4.4} \times 10^4}{\underset{9}{9.9} \times \underset{1}{2.1} \times 10^2} = 1.33 \times 10^2$

Calculations with numbers in standard form are easily carried out using a calculator. To enter the number 6.5×10^{-12} into a calculator the key sequence is

| 6.5 | | EXP | | 12 | | +/− | which displays as | 6.5 −12 |

To calculate $6.5 \times 10^{-7} \times 3.4 \times 10^{-2}$ the key sequence is

| 6.5 | | EXP | | 7 | | +/− | | × | | 3.4 | | EXP | | 2 | | +/− | | = |

The result will be displayed as | 2.21 −08 | which means 2.21×10^{-8}. Some calculators will display it as 0.0000000221.

EXERCISE 11.2

1. Write the following numbers in standard form:
   43.5,   756,   300.5,   0.0097,   0.002,   0.000572,
   97 000 000,   861 462,   0.0000011

2. Change the following numbers in standard form into ordinary numbers:
   (i) 8.6×10^7 (ii) 5.0×10^{-3} (iii) 2.7×10^{-1}

3. Evaluate $\dfrac{3.3 \times 10^{-4} \times 4.2 \times 10^8}{1.1 \times 10^{-3} \times 2.1 \times 10^2}$ without using a calculator.

4. A rectangular tray has dimensions 312 mm × 640 mm. Find the area of the tray in standard form (i) in mm²   (ii) in m².

5. Find the value of (i) 57 000 000 000 × 0.00067
                            (ii) 57 000 000 000 ÷ 0.00067.

6. How many millimetres are there in 46 km, giving your answer in standard form?

7. The number of people passing through the turnstiles for a football match was 72 761. Write this number in standard form and round it to 2 significant figures.

8. The weight on the floor of a building is given by $W = 9.2 \times 10^5$ A, where A is the area of the floor. Find the weight on the floor if (i) $A = 1 \times 10^{-4}$, (ii) $A = 0.015$.

9. Work out the following using a calculator.
   (i) $5.29 \times 10^4 \times 6.27 \times 10^3$
   (ii) $7.3 \times 10^{-3} \times 8.64 \times 10^{-5}$
   (iii) $4.41 \times 10^{-3} \times 9.37 \times 10^6$
   (iv) $4.36 \times 10^7 \div 7.21 \times 10^{-5}$
   (v) $(3.16 \times 10^{-6})^2$
   (vi) $\sqrt{(8.7 \times 10^6)}$
   Check your answers by rounding off to 1 significant figure.

11.3 Formulae

Compound interest

As explained earlier a sum of money deposited in a bank or building society will earn compound interest if the interest is added to the original sum each year.

Let a capital of £200 be deposited at an annual rate of compound interest of 5% for 3 years.

Interest in the first year is 5% of £200 $= \dfrac{5}{100} \times 200$

Capital at the end of the 1st year $= 200 + \dfrac{5}{100} \times 200$

$\qquad\qquad\qquad\qquad\qquad\qquad = 200(1 + \dfrac{5}{100})$

$\qquad\qquad\qquad\qquad\qquad\qquad = \dfrac{105}{100} \times 200$

$\qquad\qquad\qquad\qquad\qquad\qquad = 1.05 \times 200$

that is, capital at the end of the year is $1.05 \times$ capital at the beginning of the year.

Capital at the beginning of the 2nd year $= 1.05 \times 200$
Capital at the end of 2nd year $\qquad = 1.05 \times (1.05 \times 200)$
$\qquad = (1.05)^2 \times 200$
Capital at end of 3rd year $\qquad = (1.05)^3 \times 200$
Capital at the end of n years $\qquad = (1.05)^n \times 200 = 200(1 + 0.05)^n$
$\qquad = 200(1 + \frac{5}{100})^n$

In general an initial capital £P invested at R% compound annual interest for n years will produce a final capital £C which is given by

$$C = P\left(1 + \frac{R}{100}\right)^n$$

EXAMPLE 11.7

Find the final value of a capital sum of £500 invested for 4 years, at a compound rate of interest of 6% per annum.

Solution

For 4 years at 6%, P = £500, R = 6%, n = 4,

Capital C $= 500(1 + \frac{6}{100})^4$
$= 500 \times 1.06^4$
$= 500 \times 1.2625$
$= £631.24$

Converting temperature from °C to °F

On the Celsius scale the freezing point is 0 °C and the boiling point is 100 °C, giving 100 divisions between the two points.

On the Fahrenheit scale the freezing point is 32 °F and the boiling point is 212 °F, giving 180 divisions between the two points (Fig. 11.1(a)).

When the mercury rises from the freezing point to the boiling point it means that

$\qquad$ 100 divisions C = 180 divisions F
Simplifying $\qquad$ 5 divisions C = 9 divisions F
that is $\qquad$ 1 division C = $\frac{9}{5}$ divisions F as shown in Fig. 11.1(b)
$\qquad$ c divisions C = $\frac{9}{5}$c divisions F

This is $\frac{9}{5}$c above 32 °F so that the Fahrenheit temperature f is

$\qquad f = \frac{9}{5}c + 32$

Fig. 11.1

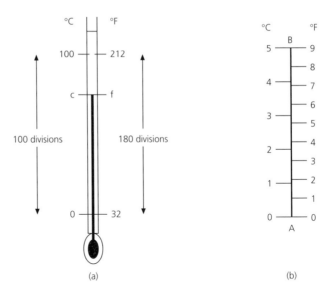

(a)   (b)

EXAMPLE 11.8

Use the formula to convert 45 °C to Fahrenheit.

Solution

Substitute c = 45 into $f = \frac{9}{5}c + 32$

$$= \frac{9}{5} \times 45 + 32$$
$$= 9 \times 9 + 32$$
$$= 113\ °F$$

Rearranging formulae

The formula $f = \frac{9}{5}c + 32$ is used to calculate the value of f on the Fahrenheit scale when the value of c on the Celsius scale is known. f is called the *subject* of the formula. In this formula the right-hand side consists of two parts separated by a + sign. Each part is called a *term*. Terms are separated by a + sign or a − sign.

If the value of c is required for a known value of f, the formula has to be rearranged to make c the subject.

Rearranging a formula requires a number of steps. What is essential to remember is that **any change made on one side of a formula must also be made on the other side**.

A number of examples of rearranging formulae are now considered.

(i) The formula $A = L \times W$ for the area of a rectangle is rearranged to make L the subject.

Switch the formula around so that the term containing L, the new subject, is on the left.

$$L \times W = A$$

There is only one term on the left so divide both sides by W.

$$\frac{L \times W}{W} = \frac{A}{W}$$

$$L = \frac{A}{W}$$

(ii) The formula $s = \dfrac{d}{t}$ for speed is rearranged to make d the subject.

Switch the formula around, so that the term containing d is on the left side

$$\frac{d}{t} = s$$

There is only one term on the left side, so multiply both sides by t

$$\frac{d}{t} \times t = s \times t$$

$$d = st$$

A formula such as $d = s \times t$ can easily be rearranged using the triangle

By looking at the positions of the letters the formulae are

$$s = \frac{d}{t}, \quad t = \frac{d}{s}, \quad d = s \times t$$

(iii) The formula $P = 2L + 2W$ for the perimeter of a rectangle is rearranged making W the subject.

Switch the formula around so that W appears on the left side.

$$2L + 2W = P$$

There are two terms on the left side, so that 2L is subtracted from both sides.

$$2L - 2L + 2W = P - 2L$$

$$2W = P - 2L$$

Divide both sides by 2, by placing the two terms on the right in a bracket, to show that **all** the right side is divided by 2.

$$W = \frac{(P - 2L)}{2}$$

(iv) The formula $f = \frac{9}{5}c + 32$ for converting Celsius temperatures into Fahrenheit temperatures is rearranged to make c the subject.
Switch the formula around so that c is on the left side.

$$\tfrac{9}{5}c + 32 = f$$

There are two terms on the left side so subtract 32 from both sides.

$$\tfrac{9}{5}c + 32 - 32 = f - 32$$
$$\tfrac{9}{5}c = f - 32$$

Divide both sides by $\frac{9}{5}$ to get c.

$$\tfrac{9}{5}c \div \tfrac{9}{5} = (f - 32) \div \tfrac{9}{5}$$

The whole of the right side must be divided by $\frac{9}{5}$ so that f − 32 is placed in a bracket.

$$c = (f - 32) \times \tfrac{5}{9}$$
$$c = \tfrac{5}{9}(f - 32)$$

(v) The formula $V = L^3$ for the volume of a cube is rearranged to make L the subject.
Switch the formula around so that L is on the left side.

$$L^3 = V$$

To obtain L we divide the index on both sides by 3, that is, take the cube root on both sides.

$$L^{3 \div 3} = V^{1 \div 3}$$
$$L = V^{\frac{1}{3}} = \sqrt[3]{V}$$

EXAMPLE 11.9

A cube has a volume of 125 m³. Find the length of its sides.

Solution

Volume of cube $V = L^3$
$$L^3 = 125$$
$$L = \sqrt[3]{(125)} = \sqrt[3]{(5 \times 5 \times 5)} = 5 \text{ m}$$

(vi) The Pythagoras formula $c^2 = a^2 + b^2$ is rearranged to make b the subject.
Switch the formula around, so that b is on the left side.

$$a^2 + b^2 = c^2$$

There are two terms on the left side so subtract a^2 from both sides.

$$a^2 - a^2 + b^2 = c^2 - a^2$$
$$b^2 = c^2 - a^2$$

Take the square root on both sides.

$$b = \sqrt{(c^2 - a^2)}$$

Note: The square root must be taken after subtracting.

EXAMPLE 11.10

The side c opposite the right angle in a right-angled triangle is 15 cm, and one of the other sides a is 13 cm. Find the third side using the formula of Pythagoras.

Solution

$$c^2 = a^2 + b^2$$

Rearranging, making b the subject

$$b = \sqrt{(c^2 - a^2)}$$
$$= \sqrt{(15^2 - 13^2)}$$
$$= \sqrt{(225 - 169)}$$
$$= \sqrt{(56)}$$
$$= 7.5 \text{ cm}$$

EXAMPLE 11.11

The conversion rate from pounds (£) to French francs (FFr) is £1 = 9FFr.
(i) Determine the formula for converting pounds into French francs.
(ii) Hence find the formula for converting French francs back into pounds.

Solution

(i) £1 = 9FFr
   £2 = 2 × 9FFr
   £p = p × 9FFr
   Therefore the formula for the number of French francs is f = 9p.

(ii) Making p the subject
   $$9p = f$$
   $$9p \div 9 = f \div 9$$
   $$p = \tfrac{1}{9}f$$
   is the formula for converting French francs into pounds (£).

1. In each of the following work out the final value of the original capital invested at compound interest:
    (i)   £200 for 2 years at 10%
    (ii) £1000 for 3 years at 5%
    (iii) £400 for 4 years at 2%
    (iv) £2000 for 5 years at 4%

2. In one year a tree grows 10% of its height the previous year.
    What will be the height of the tree in 5 years' time if it is 4 m tall this year?

3. The area of a square patch of ground is 196 m². What is the formula for the area? Calculate the length of its sides.

4. The volume of a box is given by V = LWH.
    Write the formula with H as the subject and hence find what height a box must be if its width is 40 cm, its length is 70 cm, and its volume must be 16 800 cm³.

5. The perimeter of a sports ground, shown in Fig. 11.2, is given by

    P = 2L + πW.

Fig. 11.2

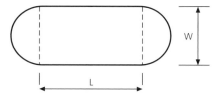

    Find the width W if the perimeter P = 507 m and the length L = 120 m (take π = 3.14).

6. The time T of one swing of a clock pendulum is given by
    T = 2√L
    where L is the length of the pendulum. Write the formula with L as the subject and find L when T = 1 s.

7. The area of a circle is given by the formula A = πR².
    Rearrange the formula making R the subject and hence find the radius R, in centimetres, of a circular disc of area = 0.163 m².

8. The simple interest I on a sum of money invested is given by
    $$I = \frac{PRT}{100}$$
    Rearrange the formula to make T the subject. Hence find how long it would take for £600 invested at 3% annual rate to reach a value of £672.

9. The cooking time T minutes for a turkey of weight W kilograms is given by the formula
   T = 50W + 20
   (i) Find the time required to cook a turkey of weight 4 kg.
   (ii) Make W the subject of the formula and hence find the weight of turkey that could be cooked in 6 h.

10. The cost C (£) of hiring a cement mixer is given by the formula C = 15 + 12D, where D is the number of days on hire.
    (i) Find the cost of hiring the mixer for 5 days.
    (ii) Rearrange the formula to make D the subject and hence find how many days the mixer can be hired for £183.

11. Rearrange the formula $s = \dfrac{d}{t}$ to make t the subject. Hence find the time (i) in hours, (ii) in minutes, for an aeroplane travelling at 920 km/h to fly 600 km.

12. Rearrange the formula, $\text{density} = \dfrac{\text{weight}}{\text{volume}}$, to find the weight in kilograms of a cuboid block of metal 200 mm × 140 mm × 12 mm if the density of the metal is 4.8 g/cm^3.

11.4 Graphs

Conversion graphs

(i) Currency
A graph is useful for converting from one currency into another. First, a formula is set up as in Example 11.11. The formula for converting pounds to French francs, for the exchange rate on a particular day, was

   f = 9p

where f is the number of French francs, p the number of pounds (£). f is calculated for a number of values of p from 0 to £20.

p(£)	f(FFr)
1	9
5	45
10	90
15	135
20	180

A graph is plotted as shown in Fig. 11.3.

Fig. 11.3

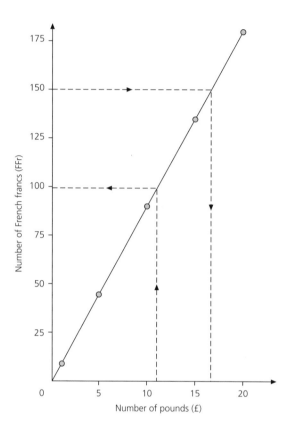

From the graph, conversions can be read off. For example

when p = £11,   f = 99FFr
when f = 150FFr,   p = £16.70

Note: With the scale used it is not possible to obtain exact conversion values, but the graph does provide a quick conversion method. A larger the scale will increase the accuracy of conversion.

(ii) Converting Celsius to Fahrenheit temperatures

With graphs that are straight lines, it is only necessary to use three points to draw a straight line graph, as shown in Fig. 11.4. In this example two points are known already, at the freezing point and the boiling point, so that only one other point needs to be calculated from the formula

$$f = \tfrac{9}{5}c + 32$$

When c = 50 °C   f = $\tfrac{9}{5}$ × 50 + 32 = 122 °F
     The three sets of co-ordinates are listed in the table below:

c (°C)	f (°F)
0	32
100	212
50	122

The graph is shown in Fig. 11.4.

Fig. 11.4

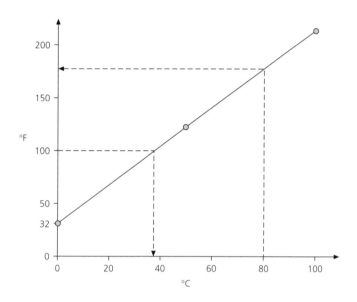

From the graph in Fig. 11.4

When c = 80 °C   f = 178 °F
When f = 100 °F   c = 37.8 °C

Distance–time graphs

The distance d covered by a car travelling at a speed of s in a time t is given by

d = st

Consider a car   (i) travelling for 4 hours at 60 km/h, then
(ii) stopping for 1 h, then
(iii) returning to the starting point in 3 hours.

(i)   For the first part of the journey, using the formula d = st
when t = 0   d = 0   which is the start of the journey
t = 2 h   d = 60 × 2 = 120 km
t = 4 h   d = 60 × 4 = 240 km

The graph of distance against time for this part of the journey is shown in Fig. 11.5 by the line AB.

Only three points are required because at a steady speed the graph will be a straight line.

Fig. 11.5

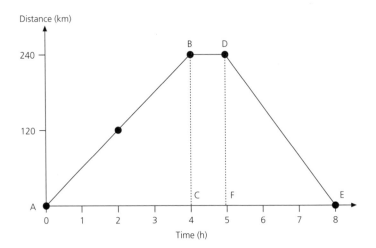

The gradient of AB is given by $\dfrac{BC}{AC} = \dfrac{240}{4} = 60$.

The value of the gradient is seen to be the speed of the car, 60 km/h.

(ii) The car now stops for 1 h. Over this period of 1 h the graph is level along BD, showing that the distance travelled is unchanged.

(iii) The car now returns to the starting point in 3 hours, shown by the line DE.

$$\text{Gradient of DE} = \dfrac{DF}{FE} = \dfrac{240}{3} = 80$$

showing that the return speed is 80 km/h.

EXERCISE 11.4

1. The graph in Fig. 11.6 shows the conversion from inches to millimetres.
    Complete the scale on the millimetre axis and use the graph to carry out the following conversions.
    (i) 5 in to millimetres
    (ii) 7.4 in to millimetres
    (iii) 200 mm to inches
    (iv) 135 mm to inches

Fig. 11.6

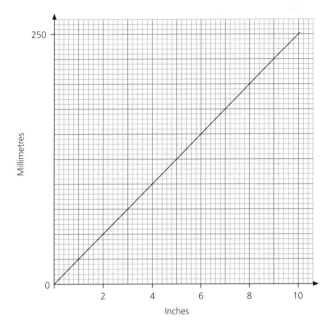

2. Using Table 5.12(b) in section 5.7 draw to a suitable scale a graph for the conversion of metres to feet.

3. Plot graphs (i) of the circumference, (ii) the area, of a circle for a range of values of the radius from 0 to 10 cm.

4. The cooking time T for a joint of meat is given by $T = 30W + 15$
   Plot a graph showing the cooking times for weights from 0 to 12 kg.

5. A cyclist travels from A to E as shown in Fig. 11.7. From the graph find
   (i) the speed on the journey from A to B
   (ii) how long he stopped at B
   (iii) the speed over the journey from C to D
   (iv) the speed over the return journey from D to E.

6. A cyclist travels at 15 miles/h. He cycles for 3 h, then stops for 2 h and cycles at 10 miles per hour on the return journey. Draw a distance–time graph of his journey. How long does this journey take?

7. A salesman drives a car at a steady speed of 70 miles per hour on the motorway for 3 hours, stops for 1 hour for lunch, then travels for 1 hour in heavy traffic at 20 miles per hour, and then at 60 miles per hour for a further 2 hours.
   He then returns to his starting point at a steady speed of 70 mph, with a 30-minute break after 3 hours. Draw a distance–time graph of the whole journey and find how long the return journey takes.

Fig. 11.7

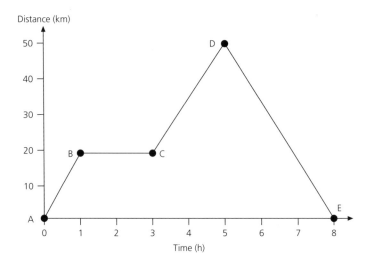

8. A man drives a car for 240 km in 3 hours, stops for 2 hours, then drives a further 280 km in 4 hours. Draw a distance–time graph, and find the speed on the two parts of the journey.

9. A bus leaves a town A at noon and travels at a steady speed to a town B 120 km away, which it reaches at 13.45 pm. Another bus leaves town B at 12.30 pm and travels to town A at a steady speed of 100 km/h. Draw both distance–time graphs on the same axes and find
   (i) the speed of the first bus
   (ii) the time the second bus reaches town A
   (iii) where and at what time the two buses pass each other.

12 Areas and volumes II

12.1 Angles

A rotating line making a complete revolution, as shown in Fig. 12.1, moves through an angle of 360°.

Fig. 12.1

360°

With half a revolution the angle is 180° (Fig. 12.2(a)).
With a quarter of a revolution the angle is 90° and is called a right angle (Fig. 12.2(b)).
Any angle less than 90° is called an acute angle (Fig. 12.2(c)).
Any angle greater than 90° is called an obtuse angle (Fig. 12.2(d)).

Fig. 12.2

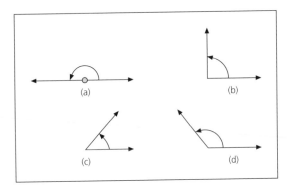

12.2 The triangle

After squares and rectangles, which were dealt with in chapter 6, the next basic shape is the triangle. A triangle is a shape enclosed by three sides. It has three inside angles. Fig. 12.3 shows the different types of triangles.

Fig. 12.3

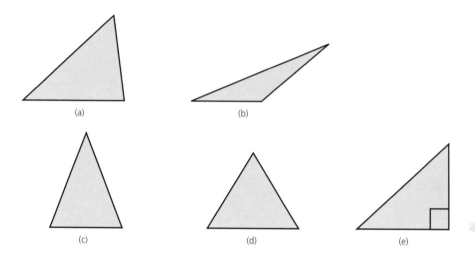

(a)   (b)

(c)   (d)   (e)

Fig. 12.3(a) is a triangle in which all acute angles are unequal.
Fig. 12.3(b) is a triangle with one obtuse angle.
Fig. 12.3(c) is an isoceles triangle with two sides and two angles equal.
Fig. 12.3(d) is an equilateral triangle in which all the sides and angles are equal.
Fig. 12.3(e) is a right-angled triangle with one angle equal to 90°.

12.3 Angles of a triangle

Fig. 12.4 demonstrates that the sum of the angles of a triangle are equal to 180°.

Fig. 12.4

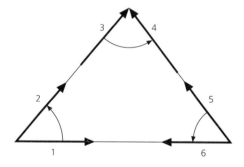

(i) The arrow at position 1 is rotated to position 2, then moved along to position 3.

(ii) The arrow at position 3 is now rotated to position 4 and then moved along to position 5.

(iii) The arrow at position 5 is then rotated to position 6.

It is seen that the arrow, after being rotated through the three angles of the triangle, is now pointing in the reverse direction, that is, it has rotated through an angle of 180°, showing that

sum of angles of a triangle = 180°

EXAMPLE 12.1

In Fig. 12.5 find the unknown angle in the triangle.

Fig. 12.5

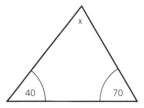

Solution

Sum of angles of a triangle   = 180°
Sum of the two known angles =   40° + 70° = 110°
Unknown angle x   = 180° − 110° =   70°

EXAMPLE 12.2

Fig. 12.6 shows an isosceles triangle with the two equal sides marked. Find the unknown angles.

Fig. 12.6

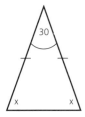

Sum of angles of the triangle   = 180°
Sum of the two angles marked x = 180 − 30 = 150°
Therefore each angle marked x   = $\frac{150}{2}$ = 75°

12.4 Pythagoras's theorem

Fig. 12.7 is a right-angled triangle, with sides of length a, b and c as shown. The side c opposite the right angle is called the *hypotenuse*.

Fig. 12.7

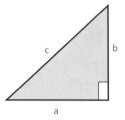

The right-angled triangle is important because of the equation connecting the three sides, a, b, c, known as Pythagoras's theorem, which states that

$$c^2 = a^2 + b^2$$

This equation can be used to determine the length of an unknown side, if the lengths of the other two sides are known, as shown in Examples 12.3 and 12.4.

EXAMPLE 12.3

What is the length of the side c in the right-angled triangle in Fig. 12.8?

Fig. 12.8

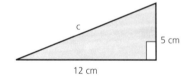

5 cm

12 cm

Solution

Using $c^2 = a^2 + b^2$ with a = 12 cm and b = 5 cm
$$c^2 = 12^2 + 5^2$$
$$= 144 + 25$$
$$= 169$$
The length c is the square root of 169,
$$c = 13 \text{ cm}$$

EXAMPLE 12.4

Fig. 12.9 shows a ladder 8.0 m long resting against a vertical wall. The foot of the ladder is 2.0 m from the wall. How far up the wall does the ladder reach?

Fig. 12.9

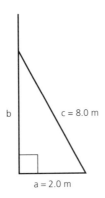

b   c = 8.0 m

a = 2.0 m

Solution

The ladder makes a right-angled triangle as shown in the diagram. Therefore

$$c^2 = a^2 + b^2$$

Putting in the values of a and c gives

$$8.0^2 = 2.0^2 + b^2$$
$$64 = 4 + b^2$$

Subtracting 4 from each side

$$64 - 4 = 4 - 4 + b^2$$
$$60 = b^2$$

Taking the square root

$$b = \sqrt{60}$$
$$= 7.7 \text{ m}$$

EXAMPLE 12.5

A plywood display panel is in the shape of an equilateral triangle, with sides of length 4 m. What is the height of the panel, given by the dotted line in Fig. 12.10?

Fig. 12.10

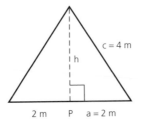

c = 4 m

h

2 m   P   a = 2 m

Solution

The vertical dotted line, which touches the base at its mid-point, divides the triangle into 2 right-angled triangles. Using Pythagoras's theorem, in the right-angled triangle on the right,

$$c^2 = a^2 + b^2$$
$$4^2 = 2^2 + h^2$$
$$16 = 4 + h^2$$

Subtract 4 from both sides $16 - 4 = 4 - 4 + h^2$
$$12 = h^2$$

Take square roots   height $h = \sqrt{12} = 3.5$ m

EXERCISE 12.1

1. In Fig. 12.11, what are the unknown angles x?
   (Any equal sides have been marked.)

Fig. 12.11

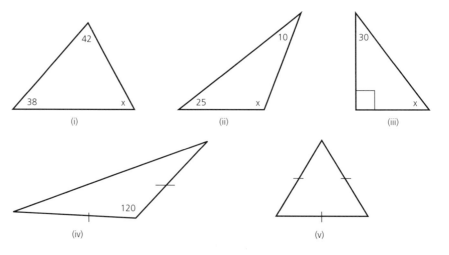

(i)   (ii)   (iii)

(iv)   (v)

2. Find the unknown side in each of the triangles in Fig. 12.12.

Fig. 12.12

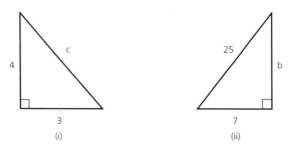

(i)   (ii)

3. A square-shaped playground has sides 40 m long. What is the length of the diagonal?

4. A ladder, 22 m long, rests against a vertical wall at a point 21 m above the ground. How far is the foot of the ladder from the wall? .

5. A group of students walk 10 km due North, and then walk 10 m due West. They then walk diagonally back to the starting point. What is this final distance?

6. Fig. 12.13 shows a cable XY joining the tops of two posts. How long is the cable?

Fig. 12.13

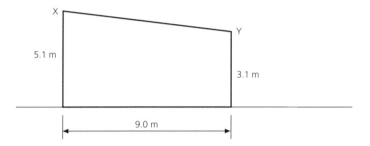

7. A triangular climbing frame is made from three lengths of wood, all 3.0 m long. If it is stood up vertically on one of its sides, how high is the frame?

8. Fig. 12.14 shows a step ladder with both legs of equal length and its feet 1.6 m apart. The top of the ladder is 2.0 m above the ground. How long are the legs?

Fig. 12.14

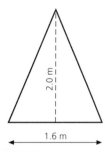

9. Fig. 12.15 shows a plan of a patio. It is proposed to lay edging stones all around the outside. What is the total perimeter of the patio?

Fig. 12.15

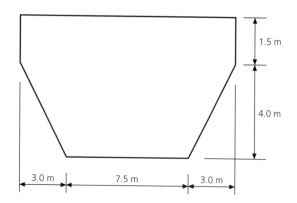

1.5 m

4.0 m

3.0 m | 7.5 m | 3.0 m

10. A clothing factory is proposing to make an apron as shown in Fig. 12.16.

Fig. 12.16

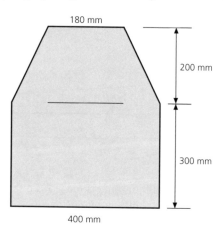

180 mm

200 mm

300 mm

400 mm

In order to cost the apron it is necessary to know
(i) the length of the sloping side
(ii) the length of piping material to be sewn around the edge of the apron.

12.5 Area of a triangle

Fig. 12.17(a) shows a rectangle divided into two identical triangles by the diagonal.

Fig. 12.17

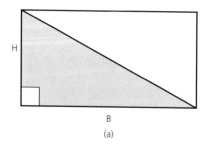

H

B

(a)

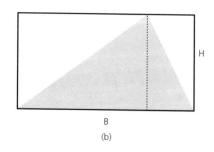

H

B

(b)

Area of triangle $= \frac{1}{2}$ area of the rectangle

$= \frac{1}{2}$ B × H

This formula is true for any shaped triangle as shown in Fig. 12.17(b). The dotted line divides the rectangle and the shaded triangle into two parts. Each small triangle is half the area of each small rectangle.

Therefore for any shaped triangle

area of triangle $= \frac{1}{2}$ base × height

$= \frac{1}{2}$ B × H

EXAMPLE 12.6

Find the area of the triangle shown in Fig. 12.18.

Fig. 12.18

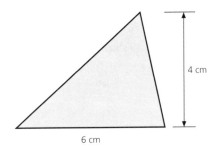

4 cm

6 cm

Solutionm

Area of triangle $= \frac{1}{2}$ B × H

$= \frac{1}{2} \times 6 \times 4$

$= 12$ cm^2

EXAMPLE 12.7

Find the area of the wall shown in Fig. 12.19, and then find the cost of painting it at the rate of £0.80 per m^2.

Fig. 12.19

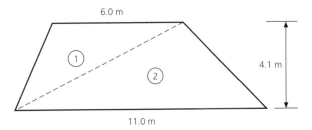

6.0 m

4.1 m

11.0 m

Solution

A dotted line is drawn to divide the diagram into 2 triangles.

Area of triangle (1) $= \frac{1}{2}$ B × H

$= \frac{1}{2} \times 6.0 \times 4.1$

$= 12.30$ m^2

Area of triangle (2) $= \frac{1}{2}$ B × H

$= \frac{1}{2} \times 11.0 \times 4.1$

$= 22.55$ m^2

Total area of the wall $= 12.30 + 22.55 = 34.85$ m^2

Cost of painting $= 34.85 \times 0.80$

$= £27.88$

EXAMPLE 12.8

The diagram in Fig. 12.20 shows a flower planting trough with equilateral triangular ends. Find the area of wood required to make this trough.

Fig. 12.20

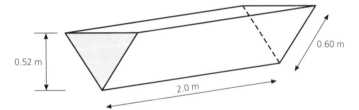

Area of equilateral triangle $= \frac{1}{2}$ B × H

$= \frac{1}{2} \times 0.60 \times 0.52$ (since all the sides are equal)

$= 0.156$ m^2

Area of both ends $= 2 \times 0.156$ m^2

$= 0.312$ m^2

The two long sides are rectangles.

Area of 2 long sides $= 2 \times$ L × W

$= 2 \times 2.0 \times 0.60$

$= 2.40$ m^2

Total area $= 0.312 + 2.40$

$= 2.712$ m^2

$= 2.7$ m^2 to 2 significant figures

1. Find the areas of the following diagrams in Fig. 12.21.

Fig. 12.21

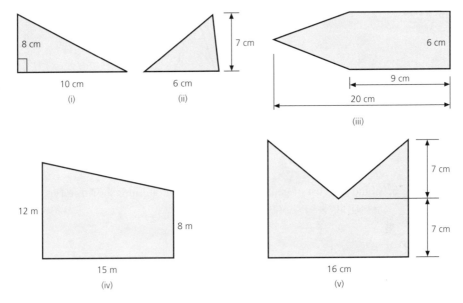

2. Fig. 12.22 shows a 20 m square garden, with 4 equal triangular flower beds and a square lawn. Find the area of the lawn.

Fig. 12.22

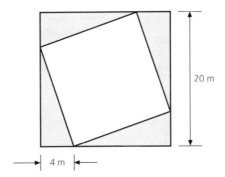

3. The hexagonal panel shown in Fig. 12.23 is made of 6 identical equilateral triangles of side 50 cm. Using Pythagoras's theorem find the area of one of the triangles and hence find the area of the hexagon.

Fig. 12.23

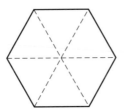

4. Find the area of a plastic toy, shown in Fig. 12.24, which consists of a triangle and a semicircle.

Fig. 12.24

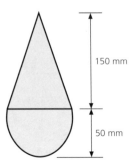

150 mm

50 mm

5. Find the cost of cementing the wall of a building shown in Fig. 12.25 if the cement costs are £4 per square metre.

Fig. 12.25

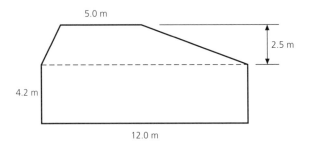

5.0 m

2.5 m

4.2 m

12.0 m

6. Fig. 12.26 shows the side view of a ramp. What is its area?

Fig. 12.26

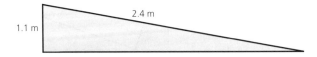

2.4 m

1.1 m

12.6 Volume of a prism

A prism is an object with a constant cross-section along its length. This means that both end faces will have the same area and shape. Fig. 12.27 is an example of a prism, with a rectangular cross-section.

Volume = Width × Height × Length
= Area of end face × Length
that is $V = A \times L$

This formula will hold for any prism.

Fig. 12.27

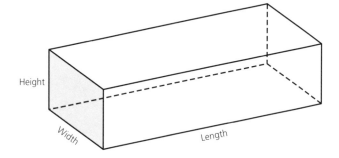

Fig. 12.28 shows examples of other prisms with different cross-sections.

Fig. 12.28

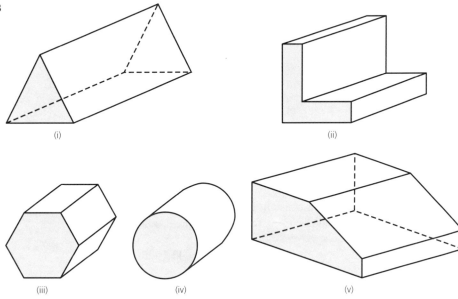

(i)   (ii)

(iii)   (iv)   (v)

EXAMPLE 12.9

A tent in the form of a triangular prism, shown in Fig. 12.29, is 1.5 m high, 1.2 m wide and 2.2 m long. What is the space inside the tent?

Fig. 12.29

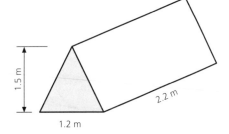

Solution

Area of end triangle $= \frac{1}{2} B \times H$

$\qquad = \frac{1}{2} \times 1.2 \times 1.5$

$\qquad = 0.90 \text{ m}^2$

$\qquad$ Volume $= A \times L$

$\qquad\qquad = 0.9 \times 2.2$

$\qquad\qquad = 1.98 \text{ m}^3$

$\qquad\qquad = 2.0 \text{ m}^3 \quad$ to 2 significant figures

EXAMPLE 12.10

In Fig. 12.30 a swimming pool is shown with a shallow and a deep end. What is the greatest volume of water that the pool will hold?

Fig. 12.30

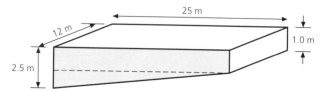

25 m

12 m

1.0 m

2.5 m

Solution

The pool has a constant cross-section shown by the shaded area.

Area of shaded end $=$ area of rectangle $+$ area of triangle

$\qquad = 25 \times 1.0 + \frac{1}{2} \times 1.5 \times 25$

$\qquad = 25.0 + 18.75 = 43.75 \text{ m}^2$

Volume of water $\quad = A \times L$

$\qquad = 43.75 \times 12 = 525 \text{ m}^3$

$\qquad = 530 \text{ m}^3 \quad$ to 2 significant figures

EXAMPLE 12.11

Find the volume of the cylinder shown in Fig. 12.31.

Fig. 12.31

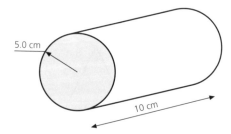

5.0 cm

10 cm

> *Solution*

The cylinder has a constant cross-section, so that it is a circular prism.

Area of end face $= \pi r^2$
$= 3.14 \times 5.0 \times 5.0$
$= 78.5 \text{ cm}^2$

Volume of cylinder $= A \times L$
$= 78.5 \times 10$
$= 785 \text{ cm}^3$
$= 790 \text{ cm}^3$ correct to 2 significant figures

12.7 Surface area of a prism

If we examine the prisms shown in Figs 12.27 and 12.28 we see that, with the exception of the circular prism, all the side faces are rectangles. The total surface area of these prisms will be the sum of the areas of the side faces plus the areas of the two end faces.

EXAMPLE 12.12

Find the area of plastic required to make the open fish tank shown in Fig. 12.32.

Fig. 12.32

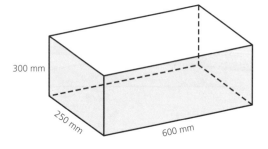

300 mm

250 mm

600 mm

Area of two end faces $= 2 \times 300 \times 250 = 150\ 000 \text{ mm}^2$
Area of front and back $= 2 \times 300 \times 600 = 360\ 000 \text{ mm}^2$
Area of bottom $= 250 \times 600$ $= 150\ 000 \text{ mm}^2$
Total area $= 660\ 000 \text{ mm}^2$

1. Find the volume and surface area of each of the solid objects shown in Fig. 12.33.

Fig. 12.33

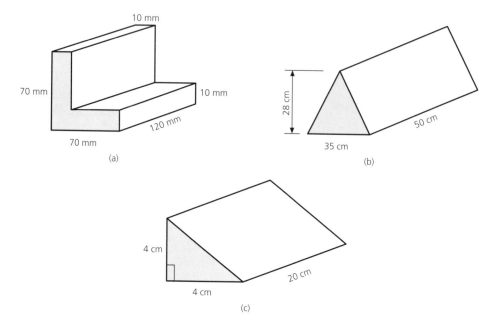

(a)

(b)

(c)

2. A disabled access ramp is to be constructed as shown in Fig. 12.34.

Fig. 12.34

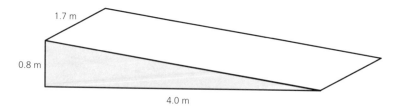

(i) Find the volume of concrete required to make the ramp.
(ii) The ramp surface is to be coated with a non-slip compound. What is the area to be coated?

3. The end of a coal bunker has the dimensions shown in Fig. 12.35. If it is 2.0 m long, find
   (i) what volume of coal it will hold
   (ii) the area of sheet metal required to make the bunker if it has a lid.

Fig. 12.35

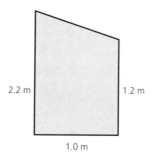

2.2 m   1.2 m

1.0 m

4. Fig. 12.36 shows the side view of a small skip.

Fig. 12.36

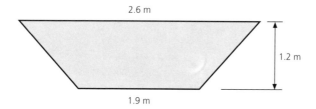

2.6 m

1.2 m

1.9 m

   (i) What is the volume of the skip if it is 2.0 m wide?
  (ii) Find the length of the sloping end and hence the area of metal required to make the skip, allowing 5% wastage.

5. A cylindrical baked bean can is 10.5 cm long and the circular end has an area of 44.0 cm². What is the volume of the can?

6. A cylindrical pipe has an inside radius of 0.2 m and is 6.2 m long. What is the volume of the inside of the pipe?

7. For the shed shown in Fig. 12.37 find
   (i) the length of the sloping edge of the roof
  (ii) the total area of wood from which the shed is constructed
 (iii) the volume of the shed.

Fig. 12.37

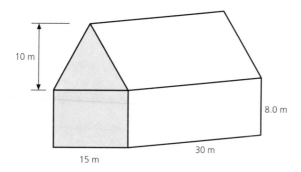

10 m

8.0 m

30 m

15 m

8. The diamond-shaped piece of ground shown in Fig. 12.38 is made up of an equilateral triangle with sides 3.0 m and an isosceles triangle of height 5.0 m.

Fig. 12.38

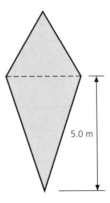

5.0 m

Find (i) the height of the equilateral triangle
       (ii) the area of the piece of ground
      (iii) the volume of hardcore required if it is to be laid to a depth of 0.1 m over the whole area.

9. A concrete kerb stone of length 1 m is in the form of a prism, with its end face shown in Fig. 12.39.

Fig. 12.39

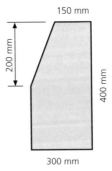

150 mm

200 mm

400 mm

300 mm

Find the volume of concrete required to make this kerbstone.

13 Data handling II

13.1 Grouping data

When a large amount of data is handled it has to be placed in groups in order to discover any trends. These groups are called classes. It is important when grouping data not to use too many classes. About 6 to 10 classes are usually enough to highlight any trends in the data.

Consider the fuel consumption, in miles per gallon, of 50 cars shown in the table below, where all numbers have been recorded to the nearest tenth of a mile.

```
43   44   45   46   46   45   46   44   45     45
44   45   41   45   45   45   44   45   43.6   45
47   42   46   43   46   46   40   45   47.1   47
45   43   44   43   45   42   47   44   44.5   44.0
45   44   46   42   46   44   46   43   44.5   45
```

The range of the data is the difference between the largest value and the smallest value. Range is used to determine the class sizes. In the above data

$$\text{range} = \text{largest value} - \text{smallest value}$$
$$= 47 - 40$$
$$= 7 \text{ mpg}$$

Since the range is 7, it is convenient to group the data into 7 classes with a class interval of 1 mpg, grouped around the mid-points of the classes which are

41, 42, 43, 44, 45, 46, 47 mpg

Because the data is continuous the class intervals are

40.5 up to 41.5,
41.5 up to 42.5,
$\vdots$
46.5 up to 47.5

The data is now grouped into a frequency table using a tally method, that is, by counting how many cars have fuel consumption in each of the above classes. The numbers of cars in each class is called the class frequency. Each of the numbers in the above table should be crossed off as the tally proceeds.

Fuel consumption (mpg)	Number of cars	
	Tally	Frequency
40.5 up to 41.5	II	2
41.5 up to 42.5	III	3
42.5 up to 43.5	~~IIII~~ I	6
43.5 up to 44.5	~~IIII~~ ~~IIII~~ I	11
44.5 up to 45.5	~~IIII~~ ~~IIII~~ ~~IIII~~	15
45.5 up to 46.5	~~IIII~~ IIII	9
46.5 up to 47.5	IIII	4
	Total	50

The class intervals are now the widths of the histogram bars shown in Fig. 13.1.

Fig. 13.1

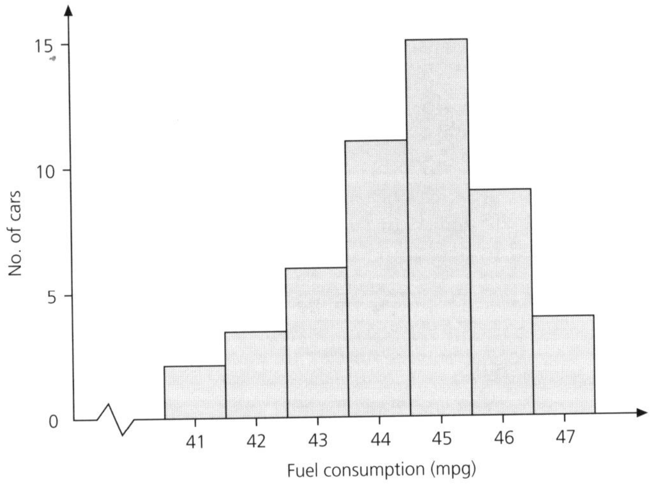

From the histogram it can be seen that the fuel consumption of the cars is clustered around 44 to 45 miles per gallon.

EXERCISE 13.1

1. The crop of apples from 64 trees was checked and gave the following yields in pounds (lb):

```
51   53   56   56   54   54   55   52
53   56   55   51   56   51   56   57
52   55   55   53   54   50   53   53
57   54   54   54   55   57   57   55
57   56   55   53   54   52   53   58
55   50   55   56   57   56   56   55
54   54   55   55   54   56   56   55
54   55   53   50   52   54   56   52
```
Set up a frequency table using the range to determine the class intervals and then draw a histogram.

2. The overtime hours worked by a group of employees in a six-week period are listed below. All times are recorded to the nearest hour.
```
 2   38   42   36   50   33   45   39   34   87
21   15   27   23    7   17   20   27    6   25
31   22    5   21   31   22    9   24   36   19
20   28   32   12   19   69   24   34   13   25
37   43   21   28   24   29   13    8   45   29
10   23   32    9   44   29   26   37   25   30
41   18   27   33   15   23   30   28   14   26
26   22   50   14   45   25   16   28   35    9
```
Find the range and hence draw a frequency table with a suitable number of classes. Draw a histogram of the table. Explain the pattern of overtime.

3. A new automatic weighing machine is set to weigh 29 grams of herbs into each bottle. The first 35 bottles were tested and were found to contain the following weights:
```
28.8   32.7   29.8   28.4   27.3   31.5   25.5
30.2   24.1   30.4   33.5   33.6   34.3   35.4
33.1   33.7   32.6   29.3   30.7   29.0   30.8
31.7   31.3   26.2   32.4   25.0   34.9   37.8
27.7   28.1   31.2   26.7   32.3   29.7   31.0
```
Group the data using the range and draw a histogram. In your opinion, is the machine performing satisfactorily? Give reasons to support your opinion.

4. The marks obtained by 50 students in an examination are listed below:
```
94   30   72   56   81   65   21   35   69   64
78   58   87   31   72   74   33   53   61   51
60   54   70   65   25   68   75   51   65   59
63   64   61   60   34   55   12   39   65   63
64   50   38   74   18   21   72   11   26   67
```
Group the data into a suitable number of classes and draw a histogram. What does the pattern of results tell you about the examination performance of these students?

5. A record was kept by an organisation of the number of people absent each day from work over a five-week period. The results were:

```
1  4  2  3  1  2  5  1  3
2  0  1  2  2  4  0  4  1
3  2  4  5  0  7  2  3  2
5  6  2  1  0  3  6  2  4
1  0  3  2  3  1  3  0  1
```
Group the data and draw a bar chart.

13.2 Average

Following on from the definitions of mean, mode and median in chapter 9, these averages are now calculated for grouped data.

Mean

In the table below, the first two columns show the age distribution of employees in a superstore. There are 2 employees in the age range 20–29 years, and so on.

Age (years)	Number of employees	Mid-point of class (years)	Number × Mid-point (years)
20–29	2	24.5	2 × 24.5 = 49.0
30–39	8	34.5	8 × 34.5 = 276.0
40–49	7	44.5	7 × 44.5 = 311.5
50–59	3	54.5	3 × 54.5 = 163.5

Total   20   Total   800.0

Because the exact ages of the employees are not known from this data, for the purpose of finding the mean their ages are taken as those at the mid-point of each class interval, that is, those in the 3rd column. In the 4th column the sum of the ages in each class is obtained by multiplying the mid-point value by the number of employees in each class.

The total of 800.0 years in the 4th column is the best estimate that can be obtained for the total ages of the 20 employees.

$$\text{Mean age of employees} = \frac{\text{Sum of ages}}{\text{Number of employees}} = \frac{800.0}{20}$$

$$= 40 \text{ years.}$$

Note: Since the total age in the 4th column is an estimate, the mean age is also an estimate.

Mode

The mode is easily found for grouped data by identifying the class with the largest frequency. In the data discussed above, most of the employees are in the second class. Therefore

modal class = 30–39 years

Median and interquartile range

The numbers below are the ages of 15 people attending a family reunion, arranged in the order of increasing ages. The list has been divided into quarters by the circles.

5 23 24 (27) 30 30 34 (38) 42 43 51 (57) 59 61 90

$$Q_L \qquad\qquad M \qquad\qquad Q_U$$

M, the middle value, is the median, M = 38 years
Q_L is called the lower quartile, Q_L = 27 years
Q_U is called the upper quartile, Q_U = 57 years

The difference $Q_U - Q_L$ is called the *interquartile range* (IQR)

$$IQR = Q_U - Q_L$$

In the family reunion quoted above,

$$IQR = 57 - 27 = 30 \text{ years}$$

The interquartile range is a measure of the spread of the data. Within its range is the middle 50% of the values. Data with a small spread will have a small IQR, data with a wide spread will have a large IQR. The interquartile range is a better measure of spread than the overall range because it is not affected by very large or very small values.

It can be seen from the above example that although 13 out of 15 people are between 23 and 61 years, a spread of 38 years, the overall range, because of a single large age and a single small age, is 90 − 5 = 85 years. The interquartile range of 30 years gives a better indication of the spread in their ages.

EXAMPLE 13.1

Find the median and interquartile range for the following set of numbers:
5 6 8 8 9 9 9 13 16 17 17 20

Solution

5 6 8 8 9 9 9 13 16 17 17 20

$$Q_L \qquad M \qquad Q_U$$

When this set of numbers is divided into quarters it is seen that M, Q_U and Q_L all lie between two numbers, in which case the mean of the two numbers must be calculated in each case. Therefore

$$Q_L = 8$$
$$M = 9$$
$$Q_U = 16.5$$
$$IQR = Q_U - Q_L$$
$$= 16.5 - 8 = 8.5$$

For grouped data the median and quartiles can be found by drawing a cumulative frequency graph, as shown in Example 13.2.

EXAMPLE 13.2

An estate agent records the prices of 45 houses sold in a particular district, as follows:

Price (£)	30 000	40 000	50 000	60 000	70 000	80 000
No. of houses (frequency)	7	8	18	6	4	2

Draw the cumulative frequency graph and hence find the median and interquartile range. Is the estate agent correct when he says that 50% of these houses cost less than £50 000? How many houses cost more than £56 000?

Solution

In the 3rd column in the table below are the running totals of the frequencies. These running totals are called the *cumulative frequencies*.

Since the class intervals are £25 000–£35 000, £35 000–£45 000, etc., the top price in each class are those shown in the 4th column of the table below.

Price (£)	Frequency (number of houses)	Cumulative frequency	Top price in each class (£)
30 000	7	7	35 000
40 000	8	7 + 8 = 15	45 000
50 000	18	15 + 18 = 33	55 000
60 000	6	33 + 6 = 39	65 000
70 000	4	39 + 4 = 43	75 000
80 000	2	43 + 2 = 45	85 000

The top of each class is used because it is seen from the table that

   7 houses cost up to £35 000
15 houses cost up to £45 000
33 houses cost up to £55 000
etc.

In Fig. 13.2 the cumulative frequency is plotted against the top price in each class.

Fig. 13.2

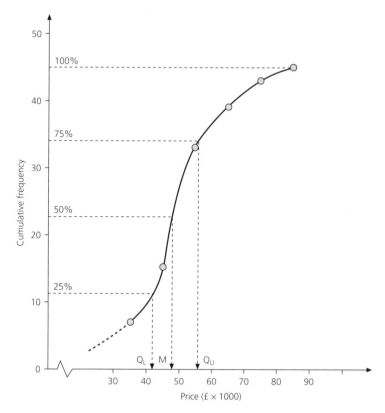

The total frequency of 45 houses is divided into quarters as shown by the 25%, 50% and 75% horizontal lines, and the values of M, Q_U, Q_L are read off the horizontal axis, that is,

$$Q_L = £42\ 000$$
$$M = £48\ 000$$
$$Q_U = £56\ 000$$
$$IQR = Q_U - Q_L$$
$$= 56\ 000 - 42\ 000$$
$$= £14\ 000$$

Since the median is approximately £50 000 the estate agent is right to say that 50% of his houses cost less than £50 000. Also, since the upper quartile is £56 000, 25% of the houses will cost more than this, which is approximately 11 houses.

EXAMPLE 13.3

Compare the prices of houses in Example 13.2 with 45 houses in another district which has a median price of £44 000 and an interquartile range of £5000.

> **Solution**

	Median	IQR
District A	£56 000	£14 000
District B	£44 000	£5000

Since the median price is greater in district A it shows that the house prices there are generally higher than those in District B.

On the other hand District A has a larger IQR showing that there is a greater variation in prices there than in District B.

EXERCISE 13.2

1. Find the median and interquartile range for the following sets of numbers:
   (i) 32, 40, 41, 36, 30, 38, 44, 34, 31, 38, 37
   (ii) 18, 11, 10, 2, 7, 20, 11, 13, 5, 8, 14, 22, 13

2. The temperatures (°C) in an office recorded on 12 consecutive days were
   18, 20, 17, 20, 19, 21, 23, 24, 19, 18, 19, 17
   (i) Find the median temperature and the quartile temperatures. What temperature was reached or exceeded on 75% of the days?
   (ii) Find the mean temperature over the period.

3. The ages of trees in a wood were checked and gave the following results:

Age (years)	0–9	10–19	20–29	30–39	40–49	50–59	60–69
Number of trees	3	5	7	12	10	8	4

   (a) Find the mean age and the modal age of the trees.
   (b) Draw the cumulative frequency graph. Hence find the median age and the upper and lower quartiles.
   (c) What percentage of the trees are (i) more than 55 years old, (ii) less than 15 years old, (iii) between the upper and lower quartile ages?

4. A factory is packaging wood screws in boxes and the number contained in a sample of 60 boxes was checked. The results were:

Screws per box	98	99	100	101	102	103
Frequency	1	15	20	15	7	2

   (i) Find the mean number of screws per box and the mode.
   (ii) Draw the cumulative frequency curve and determine the median and the interquartile range.

Fig. 13.3

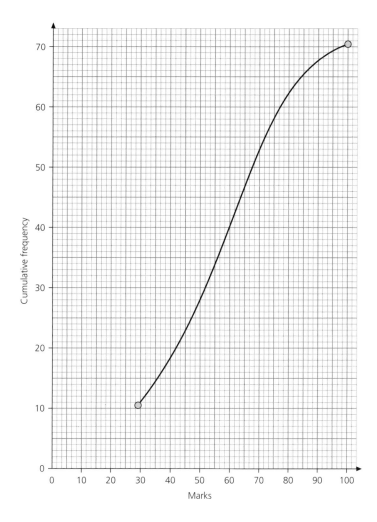

Marks

5. The graph in Fig. 13.3 shows examination results for a group of students.
   From the graph find
   (i) the number of students taking the examination
   (ii) the mark exceeded by 50% of the students
   (iii) the range of marks obtained by the middle 50% of students
   (iv) the mark exceeded by 75% of the students
   (v) the mark exceeded by 25% of the students
   (vi) the highest mark obtained
   (vii) the range of marks obtained by the top 10% of students
   (viii) the number of students who failed to reach the pass mark of 40.

6. The part-time evening earnings of a group of students were:

Earnings (£)	7–11	12–16	17–21	22–26
Number of students	5	7	4	2

   (i) Find the mean earnings and the range of earnings.
  (ii) What are the modal earnings?
 (iii) Draw the cumulative frequency graph and hence find the median earnings and the interquartile range.

7. The heights of 52 girls joining the Army were recorded as follows:

Height (m)	1.62–1.65	1.66–1.69	1.70–1.73	1.74–1.77	1.78–1.81
Number of girls	6	16	16	11	3

   (i) What is the mean height of the girls?
  (ii) Find the median height and the interquartle range for this group. Use the graph to find the heights of the tallest 25% of the girls.

8. The number of hours of sunshine per day was monitored in two different regions of the country over 40 days and the results were recorded as follows:

Sunshine hours	1–2	3–4	5–6	7–8	9–10	11–12	13–14	15–16
No. of days Region A	0	1	3	20	14	2	0	0
No. of days Region B	1	3	7	11	11	6	1	0

Draw the cumulative frequency graphs for both sets of figures on the same axes.
   Find the median and quartiles for both regions and use these figures and the shapes of the graphs to compare the sunshine patterns.

9. The wages for 50 men and 50 women are shown in the table:

Weekly wage (£)	0–99	100–199	200–299	300–399	400–499
No. of men	1	7	18	19	5
No. of women	2	16	20	10	2

Draw the cumulative frequency graphs on the same axes. Find the median and interquartile range for each set of data and use these values to compare the wages of the men and women.

13.3 Scatter graphs

In order to understand the meaning of scatter, consider whether people's weights are related to their heights. If the weights of a group of people were plotted against their heights a set of points such as those shown in Fig. 13.4 would probably be obtained. Such a graph is called a *scatter graph*. Scatter graphs are used to find if a connection exists between two quantities, such as weight and height. This connection is called the *correlation*. How close a connection is between two quantities can be shown by how close the points on the graph are to a straight line, as shown by the line AB. AB is called the *line of best fit*. In this example, because of the scatter of the points about the line, the correlation is only moderate.

Fig. 13.4

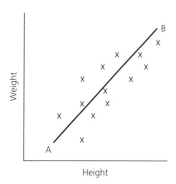

There are two types of correlation:

(i)   positive correlation where both quantities increase together as in Fig. 13.4;
(ii) negative correlation where one quantity increases as the other decreases, as in Fig. 13.5. In Fig. 13.5 the heat loss through a roof is plotted against thickness of insulation. As the thickness increases the heat loss reduces. The scatter graph shows this negative correlation. Because the scatter about the line is small there is a good negative correlation between these two quantities.

Fig. 13.5

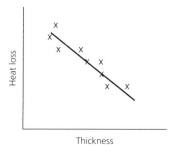

In each of these two examples the straight line clearly indicates a correlation between the two quantities.

Fig. 13.6, however, shows a plot of two quantities in which there is no correlation. There is no connection between the size of a person's head and his or her age.

Fig. 13.6

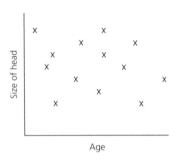

EXAMPLE 13.4

Twelve language students sat tests in French and Spanish with the following results:

French	46	71	62	83	51	68	55	76	45	50	72	85
Spanish	45	60	58	67	48	60	48	69	40	44	66	76

Check to see if there is any correlation between the results.

A thirteenth student obtained 65 marks in the French test. Is it possible to say what mark this student would probably have obtained if she had sat the Spanish test?

Solution

Fig. 13.7 shows a scatter graph of the two sets of results.

Fig. 13.7

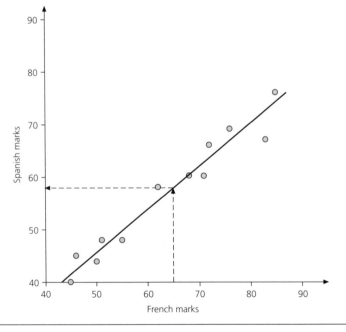

> The French and Spanish marks for this group of students show good positive correlation. From the line of best fit it is reasonable to say that the thirteenth student would probably have obtained around 58 marks in the Spanish test.

EXERCISE 13.3

1. What kind of correlation do you expect between the following quantities?
   (i) Ice cream sales and weather temperatures
   (ii) Heat loss from a building and thickness of insulation
   (iii) Household heating costs and weather temperatures
   (iv) Tobacco advertising costs and car accidents

2. Eighteen students sat two mathematics tests and obtained the following results:

Paper 1	52	70	68	52	80	63	80	75	75	49	47	82	56	75	60	65	60	60
Paper 2	45	61	65	40	70	60	50	67	65	35	40	75	50	75	47	57	49	54

Draw a scatter graph and decide if there is correlation between the marks in both papers. If so, draw a line of best fit and estimate what mark you expect from a student in paper 2 who obtained 55 in paper 1.

3. The scatter graph in Fig. 13.8 shows the intelligence test scores for 10 people recorded against their heights. Explain what the graph tells you about intelligence and height.

Fig. 13.8

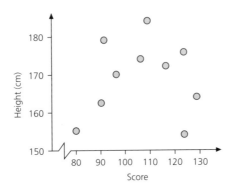

4. The fuel consumption test carried out on a car gave the following results:

Speed (mph)	30	40	45	50	55	60	65	70
Fuel consumption (mpg)	62	55	51	51	46	41	36	30

Draw a scatter graph and explain the correlation. What fuel consumption do you expect from this car at 35 mph?

5. The heights and weights of 17 people were recorded as follows:

Height (cm)	155	157	144	167	170	172	144	168	
Weight (kg)	64	63	59	66	67	68	61	65	

Height (cm)	188	153	150	180	148	157	161	184	193
Weight (kg)	70	62	67	70	63	63	62	68	69

Draw a scatter graph and decide if there is a correlation between the height and the weight of this group. What weight would you expect for a person of height 200 cm?

6. A firm decides to increase its marketing costs gradually over 12 months. Sales figures for the same period were checked against these marketing costs. The results are shown on the scatter graph in Fig. 13.9.

Fig. 13.9

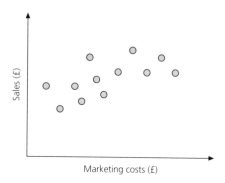

Do you think the increase in marketing costs has improved the sales figures?

Answers to exercises

Exercise 1.1

1. 2, 2, 3   2, 2, 2, 2, 2   2, 3, 5   2, 2, 2, 3, 3   2, 2, 2, 2, 2, 3   2, 2, 31

2. (i) 60   (ii) 75   (iii) 90   (iv) 12
     (v) 180   (vi) 30   (vii) 225   (viii) 162

3. (i) 9   (ii) 8   (iii) 4   (iv) 3

Exercise 1.2

1. (i) −£10   (ii) −180 m   (iii) 600 yd   (iv) −50 °C

2. (i) 1   (ii) −10   (iii) −3   (iv) 4   (v) −4
     (vi) 15   (vii) −2   (viii) 15   (ix) −14

3. (i) 48 °C   (ii) 7 °C

4. 17 °C

5. −£10 000

6. 23 °C, 52 °C

7. −£10 700

8. £80

9. 602 m

10. (a) −32 °C   (b) 8 °C   (c) 40 °C

Exercise 1.3

1. (i) 2^4 (ii) 3^5 (iii) 5^4 (iv) 7^2 (v) 2^{10}

2. (i) 2^{10} (ii) 10^6 (iii) 5^{10} (iv) 8^7

3. (i) 5^4 (ii) 6^3 (iii) 12   (iv) 7   (v) 1

Exercise 2.1

1. Numerators 1, 3, 19; denominators 7, 4, 3

2. $\frac{1}{6}$, $\frac{3}{8}$, $\frac{3}{4}$, $\frac{3}{4}$

3. (i) 1   (ii) 5   (iii) 3   (iv) 7

4. (i) $\frac{3}{4}$ (ii) $\frac{3}{4}$ (iii) $\frac{5}{7}$ (iv) $\frac{4}{5}$ (v) $\frac{7}{9}$

5. (i) $\frac{5}{2}$ (ii) $\frac{15}{4}$ (iii) $\frac{37}{7}$ (iv) $\frac{15}{8}$
   (v) $\frac{8}{1}$ (vi) $\frac{10}{1}$

6. (i) $1\frac{5}{9}$ (ii) $2\frac{1}{10}$ (iii) $1\frac{5}{6}$ (iv) $11\frac{1}{9}$
   (v) $1\frac{6}{13}$ (vi) $2\frac{1}{3}$

7. (i) $\frac{29}{35}$ (ii) $1\frac{5}{12}$ (iii) $1\frac{3}{5}$ (iv) $1\frac{23}{24}$ (v) $1\frac{8}{21}$
   (vi) $8\frac{1}{36}$ (vii) $9\frac{11}{20}$

8. (i) $\frac{11}{35}$ (ii) $\frac{1}{16}$ (iii) $\frac{18}{25}$ (iv) $\frac{1}{18}$ (v) $1\frac{5}{12}$
   (vi) $3\frac{19}{60}$ (vii) $1\frac{7}{15}$ (viii) $1\frac{4}{33}$ (ix) $1\frac{9}{20}$ (x) $\frac{8}{9}$

9. (i) $3\frac{7}{16}$ (ii) $\frac{43}{60}$ (iii) $3\frac{5}{12}$ (iv) $2\frac{1}{6}$ (v) $2\frac{37}{50}$

10. $\frac{1}{6}$ 11. $62\frac{13}{20}$ 12. $4\frac{5}{12}$ 13. $18\frac{11}{20}$, $3\frac{2}{15}$

Exercise 2.2

1. $\frac{1}{6}$ 2. $\frac{1}{8}$ 3. $\frac{2}{3}$ 4. $\frac{3}{4}$ 5. 3

6. $7\frac{1}{2}$ 7. 25   8. $1\frac{1}{2}$ 9. $3\frac{2}{3}$

Exercise 2.3

1. $\frac{6}{7}$ 2. $\frac{4}{5}$ 3. $1\frac{1}{2}$ 4. $2\frac{2}{5}$ 5. $1\frac{1}{3}$

6. 4   7. $1\frac{1}{2}$ 8. $\frac{1}{9}$ 9. 9   10. 16

Exercise 2.4

1. (i) $\frac{2}{5}$ (ii) $\frac{3}{4}$ (iii) $\frac{9}{25}$
   (iv) $\frac{21}{40}$ (v) $\frac{11}{25}$ (vi) $3\frac{18}{25}$

2. (i) 0.625   (ii) 0.222   (iii) 0.875   (iv) 0.118   (v) 1.35

Exercise 2.5

1. 400   **2.** 630   **3.** 4700   **4.** 710   **5.** 12 460

6. 56 000   **7.** 43.7   **8.** 0.0070   **9.** 18.1   **10.** 350   **11.** 61 cm

12.   (i) 46 375   (ii) 46 370   (iii) 46 400
          (iv) 46 000   (v) 50 000

Exercise 2.6

Exact answers only are given.

1. 51.1

2.   (i) 36.6   (ii) 74.7   (iii) 592   (iv) 16.7
          (v) £14 815   (vi) 13.1   (vii) 1.82   (viii) 62 940

3.   (i) 1.95   (ii) 5.54   (iii) 43.7   (iv) 2.93
          (v) 5.02   (vi) 0.347

4. Yes   **5.** Yes   **6.** £30.41

Exercise 3.1

1. (i) 3:5   (ii) 3:4   (iii) 5:6:8

2. (i) 2:5:6   (ii) 1:3:4   (iii) 1:2:4   (iv) 2:3:5

3. (i) £2000:£2500   (ii) £49:£21:£14

4. £40:£56   **5.** £1200:£2000:£2800   **6.** 10 kg:15 kg

7. 1800:3200   **8.** £6, £5; £7, £6   **9.** £24:£28, £4 each

10. 14 m, 7 m   **11.** 52 *cl*   **12.** 161 Fords, 69 Nissan

13. 60:90   **14.** 3:2:4, £6600, £4400, £8800

Exercise 3.2

1. £60 000   **2.** 350 miles   **3.** 4.5 gallons

4. £10.80   **5.** £160, 15   **6.** £168

7. 2.25 kg   **8.** 900   **9.** 180 g

Exercise 3.3

1. (i) 60   (ii) 3.0 m   (iii) 28   (iv) 40
2. (i) 5%   (ii) 16.7%   (iii) 5%   (iv) 25%
3. 55%   4. 45 cm   5. (i) 20%   (ii) 14 c*l*
6. 23   7. 12%   8. 25%   9. 16.7%   10. 5%   11. 9 c*l*
12. 59%, 32   13. 32   14. 80%   15. 7 mm   16. 260 mm × 182 mm

Exercise 4.1

1. £7.61, £12.39   2. £31.24, £7.81   3. £113.97   4. £37.95   5. £169.89
6. £4748.90   7. £25.55   8. £122   9. £110   10. £10 164, £121 968

Exercise 4.2

1. £252   2. £182.40   3. £313.80   4. £188.92   5. £158, £10
6. Shop B by £2.50   7. £1221.25   8. £264   9. £2596   10. £172, £7942

Exercise 4.3

1. (i) £60   (ii) £108   (iii) £12.92   (iv) £87.50
2. (i) 8%   (ii) 3.75%   (iii) 8.3%   (iv) 8.75%
3. £16.25   4. £10 140   5. 74.2p   6. 33.3%   7. £9240
8. £12 136   9. 12.5%   10. £300   11. £32, £21.60, £64   12. 33%

Exercise 4.4

1. (i) £7   (ii) £140   (iii) £11.20   (iv) £26.25
2. £258.50   3. £211.50   4. £141, £35.25   5. £14 100   6. £88.13   7. £105

Exercise 4.5

1. £117.88   2. £55.85, £13.96   3. £32.27   4. £116.75

Exercise 4.6

1. 737.5 Dm   **2.** 935 360 L   **3.** £400   **4.** 1365.51 FFr   **5.** 1425 FFr

Exercise 5.1

1. cm, m, mm, mm, cm, km, m, cm, m, m

2. (i) 12 500 m   (ii) 5630 cm   (iii) 8610 mm   (iv) 1436 cm

3. (i) 12 100 mm   (ii) 461 cm   (iii) 4.50 m   (iv) 0.325 m
(v) 0.39   (vi) 41 m

4. 21   **5.** 9, 57 mm   **6.** Yes   **7.** 200 mm

Exercise 5.2

2. (i) and (iii)

Exercise 5.3

1. kg, tonnes, kg, g, g or mg

2. (i) 11 240 kg   (ii) 0.56 kg   (iii) 27.56 t   (iv) 920 g   (v) 4.46 g
(vi) 72.95 kg   (vii) 4970 mg   (viii) 5130 mg   (ix) 79.187 g

3. 50   **4.** (i) 1000 g   (ii) 143 g   **5.** 50 days

6. 15 kg, 120   **7.** 15 000 mg

Exercise 5.4

1. (i) 367 ha   (ii) 3 670 000 m²

2. 60 000 cm²   **3.** 0.36 m²   **4.** 35 300 mm²   **5.** 2.1 m²

Exercise 5.5

1. l, m³ or l, ml, ml, m³, l, ml

2. (i) 2200 l (ii) 5.6 l (iii) 4.33 m³   (iv) 2000 cl
(v) 6.7 ml (vi) 600 ml (vii) 1.24 l

3. 50   **4.** 6   **5.** 40 l

Exercise 5.6

2. (i) 87.6 mm   (ii) 11.4 kg   (iii) 1.61 fl oz   (iv) 76.7 g   (v) 42.8 pt

3. 54.6 *l*   **4.** −5.5%   **5.** 114 m*l*   **6.** 480 kg within limit

7. 64.4 km   **8.** 1.91 m   **9.** the 42 kg boy, 2.5 kg

Exercise 5.7

1.   (i) 9 km   (ii) 75 cm   (iii) 20 lb   (iv) 8 in   (v) 4.5 kg
     (vi) 50 mm   (vii) 12 m   (viii) 13.5 *l*   (ix) 7 t   (x) 90 cm

2. 25 cm × 15 cm   **3.** 50 lb

4. 0.75 kg, 50 g, 125 g, 300 g, 75 g, 100 m*l*   **5.** 2250 *l*

Exercise 5.8

1. 83, 23, 1, −29, −51   **2.** 106, 39, −9, −72

3. 43 °F, 50 °F, 57 °F, 53 °F

Exercise 6.1

1.   (i) 32 m^2, 24 m   (ii) 10 ft^2, 13 ft
     (iii) $\frac{1}{10}$ m^2, 1$\frac{17}{20}$ m   (iv) 9.7 m^2, 12.6 cm

2.   (i) 96 cm^2 (ii) 66 m^2 (iii) 48 m^2 (iv) 24.6 m^2

3. 75   **4.** 384   **5.** 419, 42 m   **6.** 3   **7.** 17

Exercise 6.2

1. (i) 24 m^3 (ii) 90 cm^3 (iii) 16 ft^3

2. 192   **3.** 3570 cm^3 **4.** 6250 cm^3, 208

5. (i) 63 m^2 (ii) 27 m^2 (iii) 108   (iv) 81 m^3

6. 60 m^3, 9, 3 m^3 **7.** 4 m^3, 20   **8.** 144   **9.** 0.14 m^3

Exercise 7.1

1. 1:200, 5.0 m   **2.** 1:250, 60 cm × 48 cm, 8.8 cm   **3.** 15 cm

Exercise 7.3

1. 1:1 175 000, 1.19 cm   **2.** 29.5 km, 14 cm   **3.** 10.5 km   **4.** 35 km

5. 35 km, 21 km   **6.** 1:12 500 000, 375 km, 10 cm

7. 1:25 000, 0.9 km   **8.** 78 km   **9.** 17.25 km

Exercise 8.1

1. 42 cm³   **2.** 0.32 m²   **3.** 9.6 km   **4.** 10 miles   **5.** 4.3p

6. 31 cm, 79 cm²   **7.** 72 km   **8.** 380 cm², 69 cm   **9.** £150   **10.** 4.5 m²

Exercise 8.2

1. 0.5, 1, 2, 5, 10, 20, 100; 0.05, 0.1, 0.2, 0.5, 1, 2, 10

3. 3, £43   **4.** 2 °C, 108 °F   **5.** 53 cm³   **6.** (i) 90 km   (ii) 4.3 h

7. £110, 8.3%   **8.** (i) £10   (ii) £2

Exercise 9.1

8. (i) 73   (ii) 0 to 5   (iii) 2   (iv) 11.0%, 61.6%, 0%

Exercise 9.2

1.   (i) 5.9, 5, 5, 6
         (ii) 36.4, there is no mode, 33, 57
         (iii) 8.0, 8, 8, 12

2. 10, 12.3, 12, 7

3. £23 000, £18 000, the median

4. (i) 22   (ii) 30   (iii) 20

5. (i) 31.2, there is no mode, 30,   (ii) 32

6. £128 000   **7.** 1.76 m   **8.** 68

9.

	Mean	Range
A	£14.33	£14.38
B	£14.30	£3.14

10.

	Mean	Range
1	70.3	71
2	63.3	39

Exercise 10.1

1. 18 t **2.** (i) 3, 4, 5 (ii) £60 000

3. 12 c*l* **4.** £40 **5.** £924 **6.** £16 000

7. 4 **8.** 2.8 m **9.** 40 m*l* **10.** £12 000

11. £1440, £2096 **12.** £7500, £10 000, £12 500

Exercise 10.2

1. 6.7 h **2.** 6 days **3.** 18 **4.** 30 **5.** 144 **6.** 25

Exercise 10.3

1. £1200 **2.** £40 **3.** £30 **4.** £90 **5.** £2 **6.** £800, £640

Exercise 10.4

1. £220.50 **2.** £191.02 **3.** (i) £86.20 (ii) £80 **4.** £60.87, £63.91

5. £70.29, £82.59 **6.** (i) £92.70 (ii) £97.33

Exercise 10.5

1. (i) 10 m/s (ii) 36 km/h

2. 5000 gal/h, 83 gal/min

3. (i) 8.0 km/*l* (ii) 22.6 mpg

4. 9.0 g/cm^3, 9000 kg/m^3

5. (i) 0.20 m^3/min (ii) 3.3 *l*/s

6. 1000 kg/m^3 **7.** 925 kg/m^3 **8.** 1090 kg/m^3

9. 12 km/*l* **10.** 79 km/h

Exercise 10.6

1. 34.5 m*l* (±0.05), 135 m*l* (±0.5)

2. 64.4 cm (±0.05) **3.** 33.85 (±0.05)

4. 2.6 (±0.05) **5.** 73 lb/in^3 (±0.5)

Exercise 10.7

1. 21.5 cm–22.5 cm, 14.5 cm–15.5 cm   **2.** 312 cm^2, 349 cm^2

3. 1645 mg–1655 mg   **4.** 212.5 cm–217.5 cm, 61.5 cm–62.5 cm

5. 8.0 cm, 10.0 cm   **6.** 25   **7.** 12

Exercise 11.1

1. (i) 6^9 (ii) 10   (iii) 5^{-5} (iv) 5^2 (v) 7^2
(vi) 8^{-3} (vii) 5^5 (viii) 1   (ix) 10^8

2. (i) $\frac{1}{8^2}$ (ii) $\frac{1}{6}$ (iii) $\frac{1}{10^2}$ (iv) 7^6 (v) 10^3

3. (i) 2   (ii) 25   (viii) 729   (iv) 4   (v) $\frac{1}{3}$
(vi) 32   (vii) $\frac{3}{2}$

Exercise 11.2

1. 4.35×10^1, 7.56×10^2, 3.005×10^2, 9.7×10^{-3}, 2.0×10^{-3},
5.72×10^{-4}, 9.7×10^7, 8.61462×10^5, 1.1×10^{-6}

2. (i) 86 000 000   (ii) 0.005   (iii) 0.27   **3.** 6.0×10^5

4. (i) 2.00×10^5 (ii) 2.00×10^{-1} **5.** (i) 3.8×10^8 (ii) 8.5×10^{13}

6. 4.6×10^7 **7.** 7.3×10^4 **8.** (i) 92   (ii) 13 800

9. (i) 3.32×10^8 (ii) 6.3×10^{-7} (iii) 41 300   (iv) 6.05×10^{11}
(v) 9.99×10^{-12} (vi) 2.95×10^3

Exercise 11.3

1. (i) £242   (ii) £1157.63   (iii) £432.98   (iv) £2433.30

2. 6.4 m   **3.** 14 m   **4.** 6 cm   **5.** 85 m   **6.** 0.25   **7.** 0.228 m   **8.** 4 years

9. (i) 220 min   (ii) 6.8 kg   **10.** (i) £75   (ii) 14 days

11. (i) 0.65 h   (ii) 39 min   **12.** 0.60 kg

Exercise 11.4

1. (i) 125 mm   (ii) 185 mm   (iii) 8 in   (iv) 5.4 in

5. (i) 20 km/h   (ii) 2 h   (iii) 15 km/h   (iv) 16.7 km/h

6. 9.5 h   **7.** 5 h 30 min   **8.** 80 km/h, 70 km/h

9. (i) 69 km/h   (ii) 13.42 pm   (iii) 69 from A at 13.01 pm

Exercise 12.1

1. (i) 100°   (ii) 145°   (iii) 60°   (iv) 30°   (v) 60°

2. (i) 5   (ii) 24

3. 56.6 m   **4.** 6.6 m   **5.** 14 km   **6.** 9.2 m   **7.** 2.6 m   **8.** 2.2 m

9. 34 m   **10.** (i) 228 mm   (ii) 1640 mm

Exercise 12.2

1. (i) 40 cm²   (ii) 21 cm²   (iii) 87 cm²   (iv) 150 m²   (v) 168 cm²

2. 272 m²   **3.** 6495 cm²   **4.** 15 400 mm²   **5.** £286.60 cm²   **6.** 1.17 m²

Exercise 12.3

1. (a) 168 000 mm³, 38 800 mm²
   (b) 24 500 mm³, 4950 cm²
   (c) 160 cm³, 270 cm²

2. (i) 2.7 m³   (ii) 6.9 m²

3. (i) 3.4 m³   (ii) 15.0 m²

4. (i) 5.4 m³   (ii) 14.95 m²

5. 462 cm²   **6.** 0.78 m³

7. (i) 12.5 m   (ii) 2070 m²   (iii) 5850 m³

8. (i) 2.60 m   (ii) 11.4 m²   (iii) 1.14 m³   **9.** 0.105 m³

Exercise 13.2

1. (i) 37, 8   (ii) 11, 8.5

2. (i) 19 °C, 18 °C, 20.5 °C   (ii) 19.6 °C

3. (a) 36.9 years   (b) 37 years, 26 years, 48 years   (c) (i) 7   (ii) 6   (iii) 25

4. (i) 100, 100   (ii) 100, 2

5. (i) 70   (ii) 56   (iii) 31   (iv) 39.5
   (v) 70.5   (vi) 100   (vii) 81 to 100   (viii) 8

6. (i) £14.80, £20   (ii) £12–£16   (iii) 14.5, 7.3

7. (i) 1.707 m   (ii) 1.705 m, 0.067 m, 1.738 m to 1.815 m

8.

	Median	IQR
A	8.25	1.50
B	8.25	3.55

9.

	Median	IQR
Men	£296	£130
Women	£230	£125

Exercise 13.3

2. 45   **4.** 61 mpg   **5.** 72.5 kg

Index